PRENTICE HALL
LITERATURE

PENGUIN  EDITION

Reader's Notebook
English Learner's Version

Grade Six

PEARSON

Prentice
Hall

Upper Saddle River, New Jersey
Boston, Massachusetts

ISBN 0-13-165081-5

1 2 3 4 5 6 7 8 9 10   08 07 06 05 04

ACKNOWLEDGMENTS

Grateful acknowledgment is made to the following for copyrighted material:

Airmont Publishing Company, Inc.
"Water" from *The Story of My Life* by Helen Keller. Copyright © 1965 by Airmont Publishing Company, Inc.

Dr. Ricardo E. Alegria
"The Three Wishes" from *The Three Wishes: A Collection of Puerto Rican Folktales*, selected and adapted by Ricardo E. Alegria. Copyright © 1969 by Ricardo E. Alegria.

The American Society for the Prevention of Cruelty to Animals
"Animaland" copyright © 2005 The American Society for the Prevention of Cruelty to Animals. Reprinted with permission of the ASPCA. All rights reserved.

The Associated Press
"36 Beached Whales Die in St. Martin" by Staff from *tnew.onepaper.com*. Reprinted by permission.

Susan Bergholz Literary Services
"Names/Nombres, " copyright © 1985 by Julia Alvarez. First published in *Nuestro*. March, 1985. All rights reserved.

Brandt & Hochman Literary Agents, Inc.
"Wilbur Wright and Orville Wright" by Stephen Vincent Benet, from *A Book of Americans* by Rosemary and Stephen Vincent Benet. Copyright © 1933 by Rosemary and Stephen Vincent. Copyright renewed © by Rosemary Carr Benet. Reprinted by permission of Brandt & Hochman Literary Agents, Inc.

John Brewton, George M. Blackburn & Lorraine A. Blackburn
"Limerick (Accidents—More or Less Fatal)." Copyright © 1965 by Sara and John E. Brewton. Reprinted by permission of Brewton, Blackburn and Blackburn.

Chronicle Books
From "Oranges" by Gary Soto. Copyright © 1995 by Gary Soto. Used with permission of Chronicle Books, LLC, San Francisco, CA. Visit www.chroniclebooks.com.

Curtis Brown, Ltd.
From "Adventures of Isabel" by Ogden Nash. Copyright © 1951 by Ogden Nash. First appeared in *Parents Keep Out*. Published by Little, Brown & Company. "Greyling" by Jane Yolen from *Greyling: A Picture Story from the Islands*. Copyright 1968, 1996 by Jane Yolen. First published by Penguin Putnam.

Dell Publishing, a division of Random House, Inc.
"The Tail" from *Funny You Should Ask* by David Gale, Editor. Copyright © 1992 by Joyce Hansen.

Dial Books for Young Readers
"Gluskabe and Old Man Winter: Abenaki" by Joseph Bruchac from *Pushing Up the Sky*. Copyright © 2000 by Joseph Bruchac, text.

Doubleday, a division of Random House, Inc.
"Child on Top of a Greenhouse" by Theodore Roethke from *The Collected Poems of Theodore Roethke*, copyright © 1946 by Editorial Publications, Inc. Used by permission of Doubleday, a division of Random House, Inc.

Paul S. Eriksson
"My Papa Mark Twain" by Susy Clemens from *Small Voices* by Josef and Dorothy Berger. © Copyright 1966 by Josef and Dorothy Berger.

Jean Grasso Fitzpatrick
"The Ant and the Dove" by Leo Tolstoy from *Fables And Folktales Adapted From Tolstoy*, adapted by Maristella Maggi, translation by Jean Grasso Fitzpatrick. Published in 1986. Copyright © 1985 by Barrons.

(Acknowledgments continue on page V54)

Contents

UNIT 2 Short Stories

UNIT 3 Types of Nonfiction

MODEL SELECTION

from **Zlata's Diary by Zlata Filipovic**

"Hard as Nails" by Russell Baker

"Water" by Helen Keller

"The Shutout" by Patricia C. McKissack and Frederick McKissack

"Jackie Robinson: Justice at Last" by Geoffrey C. Ward and Ken Burns

READING INFORMATIONAL MATERIALS

Persuasive Speeches

"Langston Terrace" by Eloise Greenfield

"Turkeys" by Bailey White

READING INFORMATIONAL MATERIALS

Magazine Articles

"La Leña Buena" by John Phillip Santos

***from* The Pigman & Me by Paul Zindel**

UNIT 4 Poetry

MODEL SELECTIONS

"Oranges" and "Ode to Family Photographs" by Gary Soto

Poetry Collection 1

Poetry Collection 2

READING INFORMATIONAL MATERIALS

Instruction Manuals

UNIT 5 Drama

MODEL SELECTION

"Gluskabe and Old Man Winter" by Joseph Bruchac

UNIT 6 Themes in the Oral Tradition

PART 2 Turbo Vocabulary

As you read your hardcover student edition of Prentice Hall *Literature* use the ***Reader's Notebook*** to guide you in learning and practicing the skills presented. In addition, many selections in your student edition are presented here in an interactive format. The notes and instruction will guide you in applying reading and literary skills and in thinking about the selection. The examples on these pages show you how to use the notes as a companion when you read.

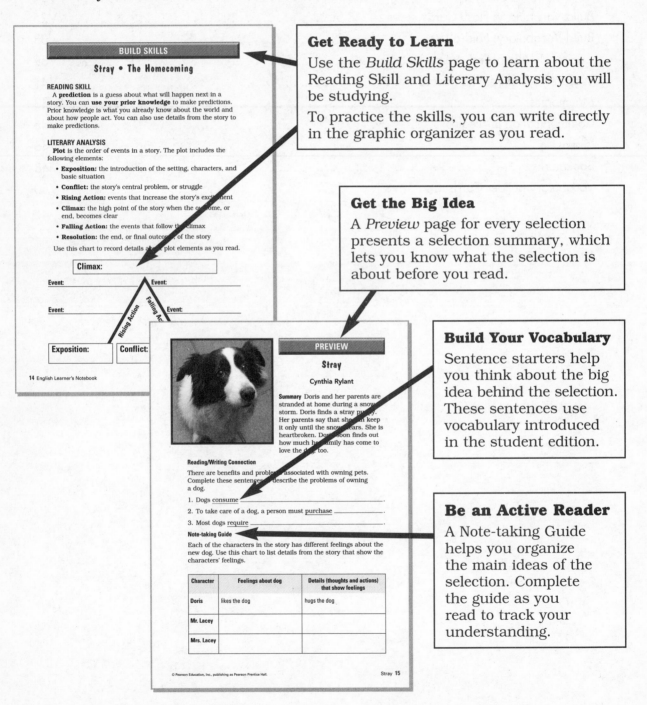

Get Ready to Learn

Use the *Build Skills* page to learn about the Reading Skill and Literary Analysis you will be studying.

To practice the skills, you can write directly in the graphic organizer as you read.

Get the Big Idea

A *Preview* page for every selection presents a selection summary, which lets you know what the selection is about before you read.

Build Your Vocabulary

Sentence starters help you think about the big idea behind the selection. These sentences use vocabulary introduced in the student edition.

Be an Active Reader

A Note-taking Guide helps you organize the main ideas of the selection. Complete the guide as you read to track your understanding.

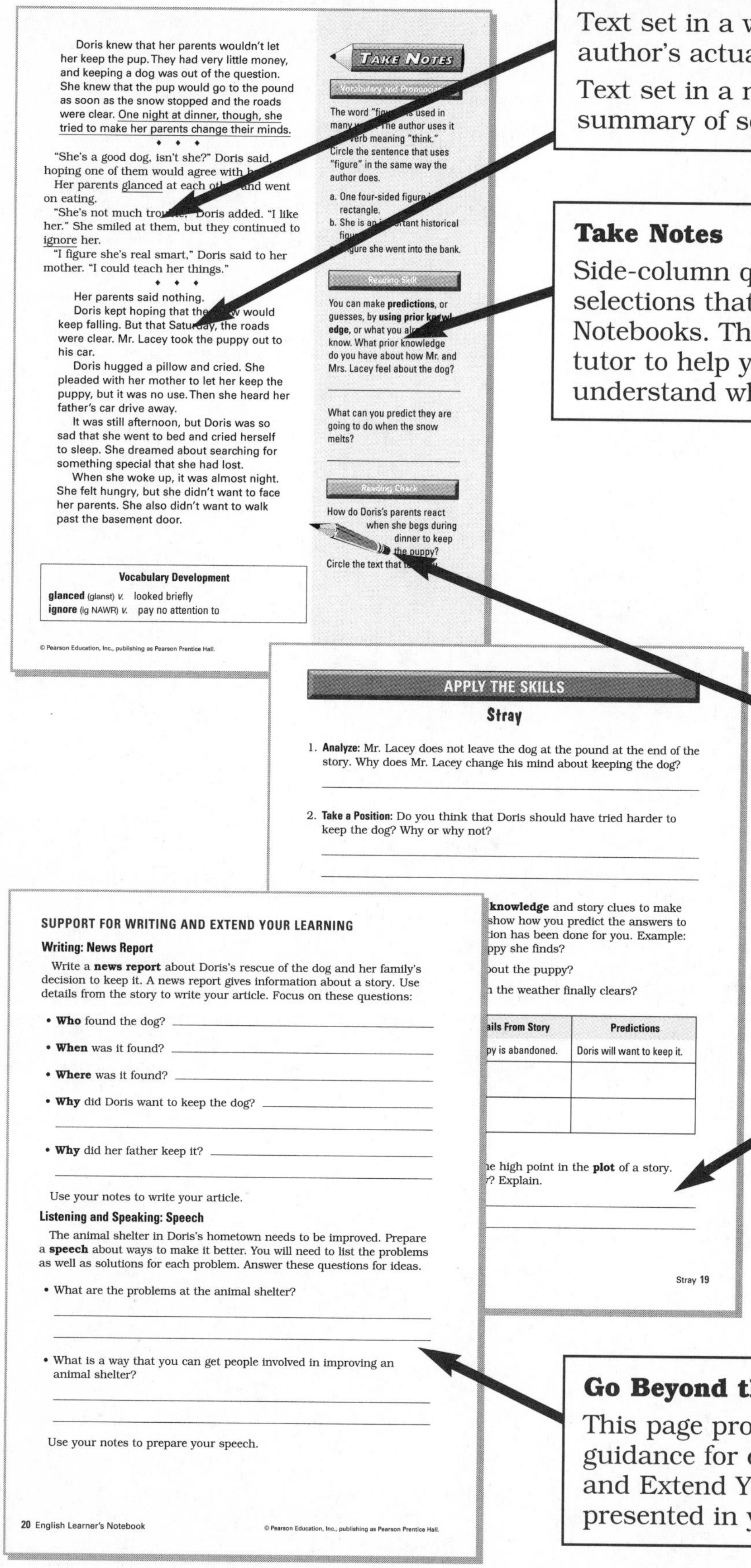

Doris knew that her parents wouldn't let her keep the pup. They had very little money, and keeping a dog was out of the question. She knew that the pup would go to the pound as soon as the snow stopped and the roads were clear. One night at dinner, though, she tried to make her parents change their minds.

◆ ◆ ◆

"She's a good dog, isn't she?" Doris said, hoping one of them would agree with h...

Her parents glanced at each ot... and went on eating.

"She's not much trou... Doris added. "I like her." She smiled at them, but they continued to ignore her.

"I figure she's real smart," Doris said to her mother. "I could teach her things."

◆ ◆ ◆

Her parents said nothing.

Doris kept hoping that the ...w would keep falling. But that Satu... the roads were clear. Mr. Lacey took the puppy out to his car.

Doris hugged a pillow and cried. She pleaded with her mother to let her keep the puppy, but it was no use. Then she heard her father's car drive away.

It was still afternoon, but Doris was so sad that she went to bed and cried herself to sleep. She dreamed about searching for something special that she had lost.

When she woke up, it was almost night. She felt hungry, but she didn't want to face her parents. She also didn't want to walk past the basement door.

Vocabulary Development

glanced (glanst) *v.* looked briefly

ignore (ig NAWR) *v.* pay no attention to

TAKE NOTES

Vocabulary and Pronuncia...

The word "figu... used in many ... The author uses it ... verb meaning "think." Circle the sentence that uses "figure" in the same way the author does.

a. One four-sided figure ... rectangle.

b. She is an i...tant historical figu...

c. ...gure she went into the bank.

Reading Skill

You can make **predictions**, or guesses, by **using prior knowl... edge**, or what you alr... know. What prior knowledge do you have about how Mr. and Mrs. Lacey feel about the dog?

What can you predict they are going to do when the snow melts?

Reading Check

How do Doris's parents react when she begs during dinner to keep the puppy? Circle the text that t...

© Pearson Education, Inc., publishing as Pearson Prentice Hall.

APPLY THE SKILLS

Stray

1. **Analyze:** Mr. Lacey does not leave the dog at the pound at the end of the story. Why does Mr. Lacey change his mind about keeping the dog?

2. **Take a Position:** Do you think that Doris should have tried harder to keep the dog? Why or why not?

...**knowledge** and story clues to make ...show how you predict the answers to ...ion has been done for you. Example: ...ppy she finds? ...out the puppy? ...n the weather finally clears?

...ails From Story	Predictions
...py is abandoned.	Doris will want to keep it.

...e high point in the **plot** of a story. ...? Explain.

Stray 19

SUPPORT FOR WRITING AND EXTEND YOUR LEARNING

Writing: News Report

Write a **news report** about Doris's rescue of the dog and her family's decision to keep it. A news report gives information about a story. Use details from the story to write your article. Focus on these questions:

- **Who** found the dog?
- **When** was it found?
- **Where** was it found?
- **Why** did Doris want to keep the dog?
- **Why** did her father keep it?

Use your notes to write your article.

Listening and Speaking: Speech

The animal shelter in Doris's hometown needs to be improved. Prepare a **speech** about ways to make it better. You will need to list the problems as well as solutions for each problem. Answer these questions for ideas.

- What are the problems at the animal shelter?
- What is a way that you can get people involved in improving an animal shelter?

Use your notes to prepare your speech.

20 English Learner's Notebook © Pearson Education, Inc., publishing as Pearson Prentice Hall.

Read the Text

Text set in a wider margin provides the author's actual words.

Text set in a narrow margin provides a summary of selection events or details.

Take Notes

Side-column questions accompany the selections that appear in the Reader's Notebooks. These questions are a built-in tutor to help you practice the skills and understand what you read.

Mark the Text

Use write-on lines to answer questions in the side column. You may also want to use the lines for your own notes.

When you see a pencil, you should underline, circle, or mark the text as indicated.

Check Your Understanding

Questions after every selection help you think about the selection. You can use the write-on lines and charts to answer the questions. Then, share your ideas in class discussions.

Go Beyond the Selection

This page provides step-by-step guidance for completing the Writing and Extend Your Learning activities presented in your student edition.

PART 1

SELECTIONS AND SKILLS SUPPORT

The pages in your *Reader's Notebook* go with the pages in the hardcover student edition. The pages in the Reader's Notebook allow you to participate in class instruction and take notes on the concepts and selections.

BEFORE YOU READ

Build Skills Follow along in your *Reader's Notebook* as your teacher introduces the **Reading Skill** and **Literary Analysis** instruction. The graphic organizer is provided on this page so that you can take notes right in your *Reader's Notebook.*

Preview Use this page for the selection your teacher assigns.

- The **Summary** gives you an outline of the selection.
- Use the **Reading-Writing Connection** to understand the big idea of the selection and join in the class discussion about the ideas.
- Use the **Note-taking Guide** while you read the story. This will help you organize and remember information you will need to answer questions about the story later.

WHILE YOU READ

Selection Text and Sidenotes You can read the full text of one selection in each pair in your *Reader's Notebook.*

- You can write in the *Reader's Notebook.* Underline important details to help you find them later.
- Use the **Take Notes** column to jot down your reactions, ideas, and answers to questions about the text. If your assigned selection is not the one that is included in the *Reader's Notebook,* use sticky notes to make your own **Take Notes** section in the side column as you read the selection in the hardcover student edition.

AFTER YOU READ

Apply the Skills Use this page to answer questions about the selection right in your Reader's Notebook. For example, you can complete the graphic organizer that is in the hardcover student edition right on the page in your **Reader's Notebook.**

Support for Writing and Extend Your Learning Use this page to help you jot down notes and ideas as you prepare to do one or more of the projects assigned with the selection.

Other Features in the Reader's Notebook You will also find notetaking opportunities for these features:

- Learning About the Genre
- Support for the Model Selection
- Support for Reading Informational Materials
- Support for Comparing Literary Works

Greyling

Fiction is one kind of writing. It tells a story about made-up characters and events. Fiction always has the same features:

- people or animals called **characters**

- a group of events called the **plot**

- a time and place called **setting**

- someone called the **narrator** who tells the story

- a message or idea about life called a **theme**

- a **point of view**

There are two kinds of point of view.

First-person point of view means that the narrator is part of the story. This narrator uses the word *I* to tell what happened.

Third-person point of view means that the narrator is **not** part of the story. This narrator uses the words *he* and *she* to tell what happened to others.

The purpose of fiction is to entertain.

Examples of Fiction		
Type	**Length**	**Characteristics**
Novel	long, with many chapters	• a **plot** with many events • several **characters** who face challenges • often more than one **setting** • often more than one **theme**
Novella	shorter than a novel but longer than a short story	• a **plot**, often with fewer events than a novel • several **characters** who face challenges • often more than one **setting** • sometimes more than one **theme**
Short story	brief enough to be read in one setting	• a **plot** with a few connected events • one or more **characters** • usually one main **setting** • usually one main **theme**

My Heart Is in the Highlands

Nonfiction is writing that gives information. It may also tell the author's opinion about a subject.

- Nonfiction is about real people, events, or ideas.

- Nonfiction gives information from the **author's perspective**. The author's perspective is the way he or she sees things. The **tone** of the writing is the author's attitude or feelings about a topic.

- Nonfiction writers may have several reasons for writing, called the **writer's purpose**.

Nonfiction is written to do the following:

- explain

- persuade

- inform

- entertain

Examples of Nonfiction	
Examples	**Characteristics**
Biography	the story of a person's life told by someone else
Autobiography	the story of the author's life
Letter	written message from one person to another to share information, thoughts, or feelings
Journal or diary	written record of daily events and of the writer's thoughts and feelings
Essay	a brief written work that tells the author's opinion
Informational text	written work that gives information. Textbooks, applications, instructions, manuals are examples.
Speech	written work meant to be spoken to an audience

Greyling

Jane Yolen

Summary A fisherman and his wife cannot have a child. One day the fisherman brings home a seal pup. The seal turns into a child they name Greyling. They do not let Grayling go into the sea. One day Greyling has to save his father. He finds out what he really is when he jumps into the sea.

Note-taking Guide

Characters in fiction have wants and needs. Fill in this chart to record what the characters in this story want.

What the Wife Wants	What the Fisherman Wants	What Greyling Wants
She wants a child. She wants her child never to go into the sea.		

Greyling
Jane Yolen

Have you ever found treasures at the seashore—seashells; bits of smooth, colored, glass; or colored pebbles and stones? In "Greyling," Jane Yolen writes about a fisherman who finds a truly amazing gift on the beach—a seal pup. But this is no ordinary seal. It is a selchie, a seal who becomes a person when it is out of the water. The fisherman brings the seal home, and it becomes the child the fisherman and his wife never had. They name the child Greyling and do not allow him to go into the water. Will Greyling ever return to the sea?

As the story begins, the fisherman finds the seal pup.

◆　◆　◆

Once upon a time when wishes were <u>aplenty</u>, a fisherman and his wife lived by the side of the sea. All that they ate came out of the sea. Their hut was covered with the finest mosses that kept them cool in the summer and warm in the winter. And there was nothing they needed or wanted except a child.

◆　◆　◆

Every evening the wife weeps as she rocks her cradle, but year in and year out the cradle stays empty. The fisherman is also sad that they have no child. One day while going to his boat, he finds a small grey seal stranded on the beach. He takes off his shirt and carefully wraps the seal in it. He then goes home to his wife. "It's nothing," he says, "but a seal pup I found stranded. I thought

---

Vocabulary Development

aplenty (uh PLEN tee) *adj.*   plentiful, in abundance

TAKE NOTES

Activate Prior Knowledge

What do you know about seals? Write two facts about them.

1. _____

_____

2. _____

_____

Fiction

The **setting** in fiction includes the place where the story happens. What is the setting of this story? Underline the text that tells the location.

Fiction

Readers of fiction learn about **characters** by reading:
• what the characters say
• what the characters do
• what the characters think and feel

What do you learn about how the characters feel in the bracketed paragraph?

_____

_____

_____

_____

Point of view shows who tells the story. A character in the story can tell the story using **first-person point of view**. A **narrator** who is outside the story uses **third-person point of view** to tell the story. What point of view does the writer use in this story?

_____

How can you tell?

_____

Culture Note

Selchies (or silkies) are common in the folk traditions of England, Ireland, Scotland, and Wales. What unusual creatures are in the folklore of your native land?

_____

_____

Stop to Reflect

Why do you think Greyling is sad in the bracketed paragraph? Explain.

_____

_____

Reading Check

What has changed suddenly for the fisherman and his wife? Underline the answer in the text.

we could give it love and care until it is old enough to seek its kin."

◆　◆　◆

The fisherman's wife nodded and took the bundle. Then she uncovered the wrapping and gave a loud cry. "Nothing!" she said. "You call this nothing?"

The fisherman looked. Instead of a seal lying in the folds, there was a strange child with great grey eyes and silvery grey hair, smiling up at him.

◆　◆　◆

The fisherman immediately realizes that the bundle holds a selchie. He explains to his wife that a selchie is a creature that is human on land and a seal in the sea. The couple agree that the selchie should stay on the land because they both want a child so badly. But the fisherman somehow feels that it is not the right thing to do.

◆　◆　◆

"We shall call him Greyling," said the fisherman's wife, "for his eyes and hair are the color of a storm-coming sky."

◆　◆　◆

And although they live by the sea, the boy Greyling is never allowed into the water. He grows from a child to a young man. He gathers wood for his mother's hearth, and he helps take care of his father's nets and boat.

◆　◆　◆

But though he often stood by the shore or high in the town on the great grey cliffs, looking and longing and <u>grieving</u> in his heart for what he did not really know, he never went into the sea.

◆　◆　◆

Vocabulary Development

grieving (GREEV ing) _v._   feeling very sad about something

One morning, fifteen years from the day Greyling was found, a terrible storm comes up. Huge waves gobble up the little hut. Greyling and the fisherman's wife are forced to flee to the town high on the cliffs. From there they can see the fisherman's boat far out at sea. Clinging to the broken mast is the fisherman.

The fisherman's wife cries, "Will no one save him?" But the townsmen look away. No man is willing to risk his life.

◆ ◆ ◆

"Let the boy go," said one old man, pointing at Greyling with his stick. "He looks strong enough."

But the fisherman's wife clasped Greyling in her arms and held his ears with her hands. She did not want him to go into the sea. She was afraid he would never return.

◆ ◆ ◆

Before she can tell him no, Greyling breaks from her grasp. He dives from the top of the cliff, and disappears beneath the waves. The wild waters tear off his clothes. Even his skin seems to slough off, until he swims, free at last, in the sleek grey coat of a great grey seal. The selchie has returned to the sea.

◆ ◆ ◆

The sleek grey seal, with no effort at all, eased the fisherman to the shore though the waves were wild and bright with foam. And then, with a final salute, it turned its back on the land and headed joyously out to sea.

◆ ◆ ◆

The fisherman, his wife, and the people of the town search up and down the beach but find no sign of Greyling except his shoes and shirt. "A brave son," people say. Now that

---

Vocabulary Development

sleek (sleek) *adj.*   smooth, shiny, and healthy-looking

Fiction

The **plot** is the series of events in a story. What causes a sudden change in the **plot** when Greyling is a young man?

_____

_____

Read Fluently

Groups of words that begin with *to* and a verb, such as *be,* can act together as a phrase with words that follow. For example, the phrase *to be alone in the car* works together. *Alone in the car* describes someone in the car. Circle phrases on this page that begin with *to* and a verb.

Reading Check

Why does the fisherman's wife not want Greyling to go into the sea? Underline the text that tells what she fears.

Build English Skills

Quotation marks let the reader know that a character is speaking. One example is:

"Oh no!" she said.

Circle what the fisherman's wife says on this page.

The **theme** is a message about life. The couple goes back to their lives after Greyling goes back to the sea. How does this show something about the theme of the story?

_____

_____

_____

_____

Vocabulary and Pronunciation

Read the underlined sentence. "Great" can mean "large and impressive" or "useful." Circle the sentence below that uses "great" in the same way as the underlined sentence,

a. The book is great for finding information.

b. A great many books fell on the floor.

Reading Check

Why does Greyling return every year? Circle the answer in the text.

Greyling is gone, the fisherman and his wife agree that it is for the best, because he is both man and seal. They have cared for him, but now he must care for himself. The fisherman's wife never cries again.

Once more they live alone by the sea in a new little hut. <u>Yet one night a year, a great grey seal is seen near the fisherman's home.</u>

◆ ◆ ◆

But it is no ordinary seal. It is Greyling himself come home—come to tell his parents tales of the lands that lie far beyond the waters, and to sing them songs of the wonders that lie far beneath the sea.

My Heart Is in the Highlands

Jane Yolen

Summary The author describes her first visit to Scotland. The stone houses amaze her. She sees new homes built from the stones of very old homes and castles. She thinks that this is like writing. Memories from her past become part of everything new that she writes.

Note-taking Guide

Fill in this chart to record how the author uses memories to write.

What writers do with "stones from the past"	What the writer is "made up of"	What the writer does with "story stones"
reshape and rebuild with them		

Have you ever written about something from your past? If so, what did you write about?

_____

_____

The **author's perspective** is the way the author sees things. How do you know that this piece of nonfiction is written from the author's perspective?

_____

_____

_____

The prefix *re-* means *again*. *Reused* means used again. Write another word on this page that begins with the prefix *re-*. Write its meaning.

_____

_____

The root word *build* is used as a verb and as part of other verbs and nouns. Circle each use of *build* in the bracketed passage. Then, label each a noun or verb.

My Heart Is in the Highlands
Jane Yolen

The author and her husband first went to Scotland in the mid 1980s. They drove through the Highlands and the author loved the cozy little stone cottages and the large stone mansions. Books about local history show that both types of homes often have been built where older buildings once stood. But it is not just the building sites that have been used again.

◆ ◆ ◆

The very stones have been reused. So in Scotland history lies upon history. As a wonderful little book on the royal burgh of Falkland in the Kingdom of Fife[1] puts it: "Absorbing stones from an old building into the <u>fabric</u> of the later one is . . . a way of holding on to the past."

◆ ◆ ◆

The builders rebuild with old stones in order to hold onto the past. Authors do a similar thing when they write books. Their stones are memories of the past. Authors reshape their memories as they build their stories. All fiction is made up of memories that are decorated, deepened, and otherwise changed.

◆ ◆ ◆

As a writer, I am made up of the little building blocks of my own private history, and what I know of the world that has already been rebuilt upon.

◆ ◆ ◆

Vocabulary Development

fabric (FAB rik) *n.*   the framework of something

---

1. **royal burgh** (berg) . . . **Fife** Falkland, once the home of the Earls of Fife, is a Scottish town created by royal charter.

The author's blocks begin with stories her parents told her about when she was a baby. Then, more blocks are built through photos from her childhood, things she wrote as a teenager, and more things that she wrote as a young adult.

◆   ◆   ◆

I simply take those story-stones and use them again in any new building.

◆   ◆   ◆

Sometimes the author steals details and events from the lives of her friends, her husband, and her children.

◆   ◆   ◆

A warning—get to know me well and you will most certainly find yourself <u>enshrined</u> in one of my books.

◆   ◆   ◆

The author says most people don't recognize themselves in her books. She might pattern an animal or a breeze after them. Sometimes even the author doesn't know who it is that she has used as a building block.

The author believes fiction is like a strange mirror. A writer looks into it and sees his or her own life, slightly changed.

© Pearson Education, Inc., publishing as Pearson Prentice Hall.

TAKE NOTES

Nonfiction

A **writer's purpose** is the reason he or she writes a certain piece. What is the author's purpose for writing "My Heart Is in the Highlands"? Explain your answer.

_____

_____

_____

Build English Skills

The writer makes up a word to show how she *builds* her writing. The word is *story-stones*. Use this word in a sentence to show you understand what it means.

_____

_____

_____

Stop to Reflect

The author says that fiction is "like a strange mirror." What does she mean?

_____

_____

Reading Check

What does the writer warn the reader about? Underline the answer in the text.

Vocabulary Development

enshrined (in SHRYND) *v.*   put in a special place so that people can see

Fiction and Nonfiction

1. **Evaluate:** Do you think the fisherman and his wife should have kept Greyling from the sea? Why or why not?

_____

_____

2. **Compare:** The author in "My Heart Is in the Highlands" compares writing a book to reusing old stones. How are the actions alike?

_____

_____

_____

3. **Fiction:** A made-up story is fiction. An author often includes details that make it clear that the story is fiction. Fill in this chart with details that show that "Greyling" is **fiction**.

Fictional Details	Importance to the Story

4. **Nonfiction:** What do you think is the **purpose** of "My Heart Is in the Highlands"? Explain.

_____

_____

_____

RESEARCH THE AUTHOR

Bulletin Board Display

- Other fiction by Jane Yolen includes *Dream Weaver, The Faery Flag, Here There Be Dragons*, and *Mightier than the Sword*. Her nonfiction work includes *A Letter From Phoenix Farm. A Letter From Phoenix Farm* is about the author's writing life at the farm. It is also an autobiography.

- Search the Internet for words and phrases such as "Jane Yolen family" or "Jane Yolen education." Search the author's Web site for information about her writing: www.janeyolen.com.

What I learned: _____

_____

_____

_____

- Search the library and the Internet for photographs of the author. You may also find photographs or drawings of her subjects. You can also display the book jackets or photocopies of the book jackets.

- Search through a few of Jane Yolen's fiction and nonfiction books to find the ones that you like best. Write a summary of each book that includes the most important information.

- Watch the video interview with Jane Yolen, and review your source material. Use this information to answer the following questions.

1. What did you learn about Yolen's life?

_____

_____

2. What did you learn about why Yolen writes?

_____

_____

Stray • The Homecoming

READING SKILL

A **prediction** is a guess about what will happen next in a story. You can **use your prior knowledge** to make predictions. Prior knowledge is what you already know about the world and about how people act. You can also use details from the story to make predictions.

LITERARY ANALYSIS

Plot is the order of events in a story. The plot includes the following elements:

- **Exposition:** the introduction of the setting, characters, and basic situation
- **Conflict:** the story's central problem, or struggle
- **Rising Action:** events that increase the story's excitement
- **Climax:** the high point of the story when the outcome, or end, becomes clear
- **Falling Action:** the events that follow the climax
- **Resolution:** the end, or final outcome, of the story

Use this chart to record details about plot elements as you read.

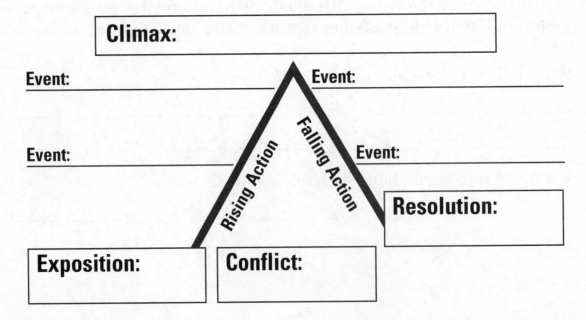

Stray

Cynthia Rylant

Summary Doris and her parents are stranded at home during a snowstorm. Doris finds a stray puppy. Her parents say that she can keep it only until the snow clears. She is heartbroken. Doris soon finds out how much her family has come to love the dog, too.

Reading/Writing Connection

There are benefits and problems associated with owning pets. Complete these sentences to describe the problems of owning a dog.

1. Dogs <u>consume</u> _____.

2. To take care of a dog, a person must <u>purchase</u> _____.

3. Most dogs <u>require</u> _____.

Note-taking Guide

Each of the characters in the story has different feelings about the new dog. Use this chart to list details from the story that show the characters' feelings.

Character	Feelings about dog	Details (thoughts and actions) that show feelings
Doris	likes the dog	hugs the dog
Mr. Lacey		
Mrs. Lacey		

Build English Skills

A *contraction* is a shortened form of two words. *Shouldn't* is a contraction for *should not*. Underline two other contractions on this page.

Literary Analysis

Exposition introduces the setting, characters, and basic situation of a story. Circle the exposition paragraph on this page.

Read Fluently

The *-ing* form of verbs can be used in phrases that describe characters, action, and places. These types of phrases are often set off with commas. Read the underlined sentence. The phrase "shivering with cold" describes the puppy. Underline an example of another *-ing* verb phrase.

Stray
Cynthia Rylant

One snowy morning, Doris Lacey was shoveling snow. School had been called off because of the storm. Suddenly, a stray puppy came wandering down the road. It looked very cold and frightened. Doris put down her shovel and called to the pup. The puppy stopped and wagged its tail, shivering with the cold. Doris picked it up and carried it into her house.

◆　◆　◆

"Where did *that* come from?" Mrs. Lacey asked as soon as Doris put the dog down in the kitchen.

Mr. Lacey was at the table, cleaning his fingernails with his pocket-knife. The snow was keeping him home from his job at the warehouse.

"I don't know where it came from," he said mildly, "but I know for sure where it's going."

Doris hugged the puppy hard against her. She said nothing.

Because the roads would be too bad for travel for many days, Mr. Lacey couldn't get out to take the puppy to the pound[1] in the city right away. He agreed to let it sleep in the basement . . . .

◆　◆　◆

Four snowy days passed. Doris thought the puppy was about six months old. It seemed happy to stay in the basement. When Doris opened the door, she would often find the pup stretched out on the top step of the basement stairs. It would always wag its tail, happy for the company.

Vocabulary Development

mildly (MYLD lee) *adv.*   in a gentle way

---

1. **pound** (pownd) *n.* animal shelter.

Doris knew that her parents wouldn't let her keep the pup. They had very little money, and keeping a dog was out of the question. She knew that the pup would go to the pound as soon as the snow stopped and the roads were clear. <u>One night at dinner, though, she tried to make her parents change their minds.</u>

◆ ◆ ◆

"She's a good dog, isn't she?" Doris said, hoping one of them would agree with her.

Her parents <u>glanced</u> at each other and went on eating.

"She's not much trouble," Doris added. "I like her." She smiled at them, but they continued to <u>ignore</u> her.

"I figure she's real smart," Doris said to her mother. "I could teach her things."

◆ ◆ ◆

Her parents said nothing.

Doris kept hoping that the snow would keep falling. But that Saturday, the roads were clear. Mr. Lacey took the puppy out to his car.

Doris hugged a pillow and cried. She pleaded with her mother to let her keep the puppy, but it was no use. Then she heard her father's car drive away.

It was still afternoon, but Doris was so sad that she went to bed and cried herself to sleep. She dreamed about searching for something special that she had lost.

When she woke up, it was almost night. She felt hungry, but she didn't want to face her parents. She also didn't want to walk past the basement door.

© Pearson Education, Inc., publishing as Pearson Prentice Hall.

Vocabulary Development

glanced (glanst) *v.*   looked briefly

ignore (ig NAWR) *v.*   pay no attention to

Vocabulary and Pronunciation

The word "figure" is used in many ways. The author uses it as a verb meaning "think." Circle the sentence that uses "figure" in the same way the author does.

a. One four-sided figure is a rectangle.

b. She is an important historical figure.

c. I figure she went into the bank.

Reading Skill

You can make **predictions**, or guesses, by **using prior knowledge**, or what you already know. What prior knowledge do you have about how Mr. and Mrs. Lacey feel about the dog?

_____

What can you predict they are going to do when the snow melts?

_____

Reading Check

How do Doris's parents react when she begs during dinner to keep the puppy? Circle the text that tells you.

What would you do if you found a stray dog?

_____

_____

A **resolution** is the part of the **plot** that comes after the **climax** of a story. What happens to the puppy?

_____

_____

What is surprising about the **resolution** of the **conflict** between Doris and her parents?

_____

_____

_____

A **pound** is a place for stray dogs and cats. Most cities have a pound where people can adopt dogs and cats.

Her parents were finishing their dinner when Doris walked into the kitchen. No one said anything. Then her father shocked her. He said that she should feed her dog.

Doris couldn't believe her ears. "You didn't take her to the pound?" she asked.

◆ ◆ ◆

"Oh, I took her all right," her father answered. "Worst looking place I've ever seen. Ten dogs to a cage. Smell was enough to knock you down."

◆ ◆ ◆

Mr. Lacey tells Doris he couldn't stand to leave the dog at the pound. He brought the dog back home instead. Mrs. Lacey smiled. There was a long pause.

◆ ◆ ◆

"Well," he said, "are you going to feed it or not?"

Stray

1. **Analyze:** Mr. Lacey does not leave the dog at the pound at the end of the story. Why does Mr. Lacey change his mind about keeping the dog?

   _____

2. **Take a Position:** Do you think that Doris should have tried harder to keep the dog? Why or why not?

   _____

   _____

3. **Reading Skill:** Readers **use prior knowledge** and story clues to make **predictions**. Use this chart to show how you predict the answers to the questions below. One question has been done for you. Example: What will Doris do with the puppy she finds?

   a) What will her parents say about the puppy?

   b) What will her father do when the weather finally clears?

Prior Knowledge	Details From Story	Predictions
Puppies are cute.	The puppy is abandoned.	Doris will want to keep it.
a)		
b)		

4. **Literary Analysis:** The **climax** is the high point in the **plot** of a story. What is the climax in this story? Explain.

   _____

   _____

SUPPORT FOR WRITING AND EXTEND YOUR LEARNING

Writing: News Report

Write a **news report** about Doris's rescue of the dog and her family's decision to keep it. A news report gives information about a story. Use details from the story to write your article. Focus on these questions:

- **Who** found the dog? _____

- **When** was it found? _____

- **Where** was it found? _____

- **Why** did Doris want to keep the dog? _____

_____

- **Why** did her father keep it? _____

_____

Use your notes to write your article.

Listening and Speaking: Speech

The animal shelter in Doris's hometown needs to be improved. Prepare a **speech** about ways to make it better. You will need to list the problems as well as solutions for each problem. Answer these questions for ideas.

- What are the problems at the animal shelter?

_____

_____

- What is a way that you can get people involved in improving an animal shelter?

_____

_____

Use your notes to prepare your speech.

The Homecoming

Laurence Yep

Summary A woodcutter gets side-tracked and forgets his work. He promises his wife he will cut wood. She reminds him not to talk to anyone. He finds two chess players in the woods. The time he spends with the chess players results in a surprise.

Reading/Writing Connection

Suppose that you have returned to your town after being gone a long time. Complete each sentence to describe changes you might see.

1. Time would <u>transform</u> _____.

2. The size of _____ would <u>diminish</u>.

3. People would never <u>modify</u> _____.

Note-taking Guide

Fill in this chart with details about the woodcutter.

Why the woodcutter goes to the woods	What is his wife's advice?	What does the woodcutter do?	What the woodcutter finds when he returns to his village
He wants to cut tall oaks.			

The Homecoming

1. **Interpret:** The villagers say that the woodcutter "knew a little of everything and most of nothing." What do they mean by this?

_____

_____

2. **Analyze:** What lesson can you learn from this story?

_____

_____

3. **Reading Skill:** Fill in this chart to show how you made a **prediction** to answer each question. **Use prior knowledge** and details from the story. One question has been done for you. Example: What will the woodcutter do in the forest?

   a) What will the woodcutter do when he sees the two men playing chess?

   b) What will happen when the woodcutter leaves the forest?

Prior Knowledge	Details From Story	Prediction
Busybodies like talking to people.	The woodcutter is a busybody.	The woodcutter will stop to talk.
a)		
b)		

5. **Literary Analysis:** The **conflict** is the central problem, or struggle, in a story. What is the conflict in the **plot** of this story?

_____

_____

SUPPORT FOR WRITING AND EXTEND YOUR LEARNING

Writing: News Report

Prepare a **news report** about the woodcutter's return. Often witnesses, or people who have seen an event, are interviewed for news reports. What these people say is quoted in the report. Fill in this chart to help you record what the witnesses saw and heard. Then, write a quotation from each witness in the last column.

People who saw the woodcutter	What they saw the woodcutter do	What they heard the woodcutter say	Quotation
Two children			
A woman			
The schoolteacher			

Listening and Speaking: Speech

Imagine that you are the woodcutter. Prepare a **speech** about why you like being a busybody. Use this chart to describe busybodies.

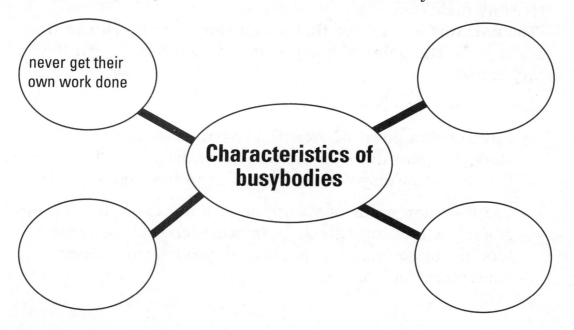

Use this chart to give you ideas for your speech.

The Drive-In Movies • The Market Square Dog

READING SKILL

Predictions are guesses about what will happen next in a story. To make predictions, use details from the story. You can also use details from your own experiences. Then, **read ahead to check your prediction**.

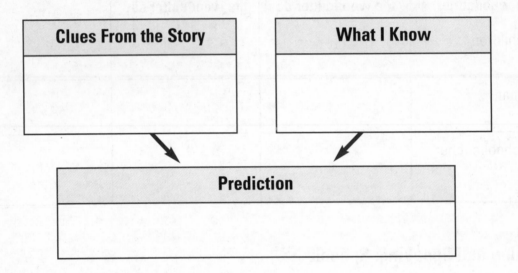

Clues From the Story	What I Know

Prediction

LITERARY ANALYSIS

The **narrator** is the voice that tells a story. Stories can be true or imagined. The **point of view** is the position from which the story is told.

Two common points of view are:

- **First-person point of view:** The narrator is part of the story. The narrator refers to himself or herself as "I." Readers know only what the narrator thinks and feels.

- **Third-person point of view:** The narrator is not part of the story. The narrator can share information that the characters do not know. The narrator can also tell what other characters think or feel.

The Drive-In Movies

by Gary Soto

Summary Gary Soto remembers a Saturday from his childhood. He and his brother and sister want to go to the drive-in movies. They know that their mother is more likely to take them if she is happy. Soto does his chores without being asked. All of his hard work catches up with him at the movies that night.

Reading/Writing Connection

Complete these sentences to describe ways that you can earn privileges.

1. Some children <u>assist</u> their parents so that they _____.

2. It is a good idea to <u>demonstrate</u> _____ to get rewarded.

3. Parents usually <u>respond</u> by _____.

Note-taking Guide

Use this chart to record what the characters do in the story.

Characters	Actions
the author	
his brother	helps wax the car
his sister	
his mom	

The Drive-In Movies

Gary Soto

For our family, moviegoing was rare. But if our mom . . . woke up happy on a Saturday morning, there was a chance we might later scramble to our blue Chevy[1] and beat nightfall to the Starlight Drive-In. My brother and sister knew this. I knew this. So on Saturday we tried to be good. We sat in the cool shadows of the TV with the volume low and watched cartoons . . .

One Saturday I decided to be extra good. When she came out of the bedroom tying her robe, she yawned a hat-sized yawn and blinked red eyes at the weak brew of coffee I had fixed for her. I made her toast with strawberry jam spread to all the corners and set the three boxes of cereal in front of her. If she didn't care to eat cereal, she could always look at the back of the boxes as she drank her coffee.

♦ ♦ ♦

The author goes outside to pull weeds from the flower garden. Then he mows the lawn.

♦ ♦ ♦

This job was less dull because as I pushed the mower over the shaggy lawn, I could see it looked tidier. My brother and sister watched from the window. Their faces were fat with cereal, a third helping. I made a face at them when they asked how come I was working. Rick pointed to a part of the lawn. "You missed some over there." I ignored him and kept my attention on the windmill of grassy blades.

♦ ♦ ♦

Vocabulary Development

rare (rer) *adj.*   uncommon
scramble (SKRAM buhl) *v.*   to rush to do something

---

1. **Chevy** (SHEV ee) *n.* a type of car.

A bee stings the author's foot. He almost cries. Instead, he pulls out the stinger and continues to work.

◆　◆　◆

I swept the front steps, took out the garbage, cleaned the lint filter to the dryer (easy), plucked hair from the industrial wash basin in the garage (also easy), hosed off the patio, smashed three snails sucking paint from the house (disgusting but fun), tied a bundle of newspapers, put away toys, and finally, seeing that almost everything else was done and the sun was not too high, started waxing the car.

◆　◆　◆

His brother comes out to help. Together they wax the chrome parts of the car. Then they start waxing the paint. They use up the entire bottle of wax on half of the car. There was not enough to finish. The boys decide that half was better than nothing. They go inside for lunch. After lunch, they go back outside.

◆　◆　◆

Rick and I nearly jumped. The waxed side of the car was foggy white. We took a rag and began to polish vigorously and nearly in tears, but the fog wouldn't come off. I blamed Rick and he blamed me. . . . Now, not only would we not go to the movies, but Mom would surely snap a branch from the plum tree and chase us around the yard.

Mom came out and looked at us with hands on her aproned hips. Finally, she said, "You boys worked so hard." She turned on the garden hose and washed the car. That night we did go to the drive-in. The first feature[2] was about nothing, and

---

Vocabulary Development

vigorously (VIG er uhs lee) *adv.* forcefully; powerfully

---

2. **feature** (FEE cher) *n.* a movie.

TAKE NOTES

Literary Analysis

The **narrator** is the voice that tells the story. **Point of view** is the side from which the story is told. The narrator shares private thoughts and feelings with the first-person point of view. Read the bracketed paragraph. Circle the thoughts and feelings the author shares about his jobs.

Read Fluently

The word *vigorously* acts as an adverb here. Adverbs describe verbs, or actions. Often, adverbs end in *-ly*. *Vigorously* tells how Soto and his brother polished the car. What other words ending in *-ly* could you use to describe some of Soto's actions?

_____

_____

_____

Stop to Reflect

Do you think the boys deserve to go to the movies after what they did to the car? Explain your answer.

_____

_____

Reread your **prediction** about the narrator's plan. Does the end of the story match your prediction? Explain.

_____

_____

_____

Reading Check

What happens to the narrator at the drive-in? Underline the sentence that tells you.

Build English Skills

The suffix -*ed* indicates the past tense when it appears on the end of verbs. An example is: The tires screeched as the truck pulled away. Circle three verbs that have the -*ed* suffix on them to show past tense on this page.

Culture Note

This story takes place in 1960. At that time, movies were sometimes called "features." It was normal for an audience to see more than one movie, or feature, at a time. Sometimes cartoons were shown before the first feature.

the second feature, starring Jerry Lewis,[3] was *Cinderfella*. I tried to stay awake. I kept a wad of homemade popcorn in my cheek and laughed when Jerry Lewis fit golf tees in his nose. I rubbed my watery eyes. I laughed and looked at my mom. I promised myself I would remember that scene with the golf tees and promised myself not to work so hard the coming Saturday. Twenty minutes into the movie, I fell asleep with one hand in the popcorn.

---

3. **Jerry Lewis** A comedian who starred in many movies during the 1950s and 1960s.

The Drive-In Movies

1. **Draw Conclusions:** The narrator and his brother make a mess with the car wax. Their mother does not get angry. Why do you think she does not get angry?

   _____

   _____

2. **Infer:** Do you think Soto still has good memories of that day and night? Explain.

   _____

   _____

3. **Reading Skill:** You made **predictions**, or guesses, about what would happen in the story. Did any of your predictions change as you read? Explain.

   _____

   _____

4. **Literary Analysis:** Soto writes in **first-person point of view**. This means that readers know only what Soto tells them about events. Use this chart to show how Soto's **point of view** affects what readers know about events. Follow the example that has been done for you.

Event	Details Provided by Narrator
The narrator is stung by a bee.	The sting hurts.

SUPPORT FOR WRITING AND EXTEND YOUR LEARNING

Writing: Autobiographical Narrative

Write an **autobiographical narrative** that describes an event, a person, or a certain time in your life. Answer each question in this chart. Then, list details about the event, the place, and the people. Use your notes to help you write your narrative.

Questions to Ask Yourself	Answers	More Details
Where was the event?		
What happened first at the event?		
What happened last at the event?		
Who was at the event?		

Research and Technology: Response

Use the Internet and other resources to find information about Gary Soto. Use your research to write a **response** to the following statement: *Writers should write about what they know—people, events, details, and lessons from their own lives.* Answer the following questions.

• What other stories has Gary Soto written? List some titles here.

_____

• What events from his own life has Gary Soto written about?

_____

• What people from his life has he written about?

_____

The Market Square Dog

James Herriot

Summary A veterinarian, or animal doctor, sees a dog begging for food in a market square. Later, the dog is injured in an accident. A policeman brings the injured dog to the veterinarian. They become worried when no one comes to claim the dog.

Reading/Writing Connection

Complete these sentences to describe a time you saw someone show compassion.

1. Some people <u>assist</u> _____.

2. Sometimes people <u>contribute</u> _____.

3. Helping someone in need might <u>involve</u> _____.

Note-taking Guide

Answer the questions in this chart. Record details from the story.

Who is the narrator?	The narrator is a veterinarian.
Where does he first see the dog?	
What does the policeman do when he finds the hurt dog?	
How does the veterinarian help the dog?	
Who adopts the dog? **Why**?	

The Market Square Dog

1. **Draw Conclusions:** Why do you think the narrator visits the dog at the police station?

   _____

2. **Interpret:** The dog runs away from people who try to pet him at the beginning of the story. Why might the dog be afraid of people?

   _____

3. **Reading Skill:** You made **predictions**, or guesses, about what would happen next as you read the story. What did you predict would happen to the dog?

   _____

   _____

4. **Literary Analysis:** Herriot writes in **first-person point of view**. Use this chart to show how Herriot's point of view affects what readers know about the story's events. Follow the example that has been done for you.

Event	Details Provided by Narrator
The dog is begging for food in front of a stall.	The narrator thinks that dogs look very appealing when they sit up.

SUPPORT FOR WRITING AND EXTEND YOUR LEARNING

Writing: Autobiographical Narrative

Write an **autobiographical narrative** about an animal that you know. Use this chart to help you. First, answer each question. Then, list other details about the event. Use your notes to help you write your narrative.

Questions to Ask Yourself	Answers	More Details
Where was the event?		
What happened first at the event?		
What happened last at the event?		
Who was at the event?		

Listening and Speaking: Conversation

With a partner, act out a **conversation** between the narrator and his wife. The narrator tells his wife that the police officer has adopted the dog. Use the chart to describe how the narrator and his wife will discuss events.

Event	How the narrator describes the event	How the wife responds to narrator's description
The police officer tells the narrator that the dog has been arrested.		
The narrator finds out that the police officer has adopted the dog.		

Web Sites

ABOUT WEB SITES

Web sites are pages of information you find on the Internet. Each Web site has an address called a Universal Resource Locator (URL).

- **.edu**—The site belongs to an educational institution.
- **.gov**—The site belongs to a government office.
- **.org**—The site belongs to a nonprofit organization.
- **.com**—The site belongs to a commercial organization.

A Web site can have many Web pages. You can move from one page to another by clicking your mouse on a *link*.

Not all Web sites give you good information. Always make sure that your information comes from sources you can trust.

READING SKILL

Web sites have special features that help you move quickly around the site. You can **use the text structure** to find the information you need. The chart shows some of the features that will help you find your way around a Web site.

Web Site Features	
Link	A connection to another spot on the same Web page or to a different Web page or Web site. A link can be underlined or highlighted text, an image, or a photograph. Links are what make the Web a "web."
Icon	An image or small drawing that may appear by itself or with text. Icons are often links as well.
Graphics	Pictures, maps, tables, and other graphic sources often featured on a Web site. These graphics often provide information, but they may also be links to other Web pages.

pet care | animal encyclopedia | bookworms | ask azula | career center | real issues | humane education | games | legal info

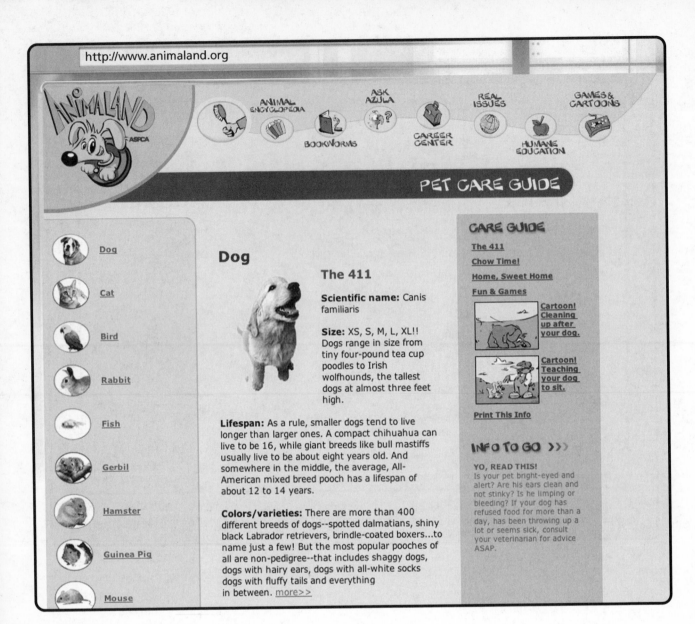

http://www.animaland.org

ANIMALAND of ASPCA

ANIMAL ENCYCLOPEDIA

BOOKWORMS

ASK AZULA

CAREER CENTER

REAL ISSUES

HUMANE EDUCATION

GAMES & CARTOONS

PET CARE GUIDE

Dog

Cat

Bird

Rabbit

Fish

Gerbil

Hamster

Guinea Pig

Mouse

Dog

The 411

Scientific name: Canis familiaris

Size: XS, S, M, L, XL!! Dogs range in size from tiny four-pound tea cup poodles to Irish wolfhounds, the tallest dogs at almost three feet high.

Lifespan: As a rule, smaller dogs tend to live longer than larger ones. A compact chihuahua can live to be 16, while giant breeds like bull mastiffs usually live to be about eight years old. And somewhere in the middle, the average, All-American mixed breed pooch has a lifespan of about 12 to 14 years.

Colors/varieties: There are more than 400 different breeds of dogs--spotted dalmatians, shiny black Labrador retrievers, brindle-coated boxers...to name just a few! But the most popular pooches of all are non-pedigree--that includes shaggy dogs, dogs with hairy ears, dogs with all-white socks dogs with fluffy tails and everything in between. more>>

CARE GUIDE

The 411

Chow Time!

Home, Sweet Home

Fun & Games

Cartoon! Cleaning up after your dog.

Cartoon! Teaching your dog to sit.

Print This Info

INFO TO GO >>>

YO, READ THIS!
Is your pet bright-eyed and alert? Are his ears clean and not stinky? Is he limping or bleeding? If your dog has refused food for more than a day, has been throwing up a lot or seems sick, consult your veterinarian for advice ASAP.

THINKING ABOUT THE WEB SITE

1. Why should you evaluate sources of information on the Internet?

   _____

2. Why would the ASPCA (an organization that gives away homeless pets) Web site be a more reliable source of information on pet care than the Web site for a pet store?

   _____

READING SKILL

3. What should you do to get more information about dogs on the pet care page?

   _____

4. Go to the home page for www.animaland.org. What button would you click on if you wanted to find out about jobs related to animal care?

   _____

TIMED WRITING: EXPLANATION (15 minutes)

Summarize the features of www.animaland.org to explain how to care for cats. Use the answers to these questions to help write your explanation.

- What is the first thing a cat owner should do to find information about cats on www.animaland.org?

  _____

- What kinds of information might the Web site give about cats?

  _____

Stage Fright • My Papa, Mark Twain

READING SKILL

Nonfiction works often have an author's opinion as well as facts. A **fact** is information that can be proved. An **opinion** is a person's thoughts or beliefs. To **recognize clues that indicate an opinion**, do the following:

- Look for phrases that show an opinion. Phrases could be *I believe* or *in my opinion.*

- Look for words that show a personal opinion, or feeling. Such words could be *wonderful* or *terrible.*

- Be aware of words that show a personal attitude, or viewpoint. Words that could show this are *always, nobody, worst,* and *all.*

LITERARY ANALYSIS

An **author's perspective** is the viewpoint from which he or she writes.

An author's perspective comes from:
- where the writer is from, or the writer's background.
- what the writer believes.

An author's perspective shows his or her feelings. It also shows his or her interest in a subject.

Use this diagram to record details that tell you the author's perspective.

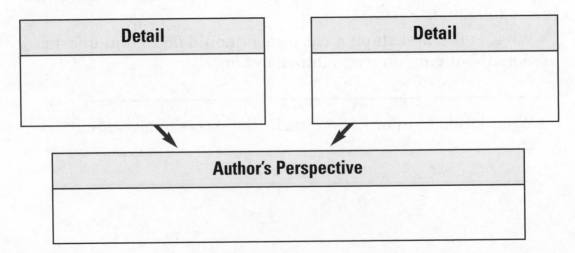

Stage Fright

Mark Twain

Summary Mark Twain tells about his first time in front of an audience. He was so scared that he had friends scattered around the audience. One friend was to laugh when Twain looked at her. The way his plan works has a funnier result than he intended.

Reading/Writing Connection

Complete each sentence to describe possible experiences that cause stage fright.

1. Having stage fright might cause a person to ignore _____.

2. A person would be too nervous to respond to _____.

3. The audience might react with _____.

Note-taking Guide

Mark Twain was known for being funny. Fill in this chart with details that show how he is funny in this speech.

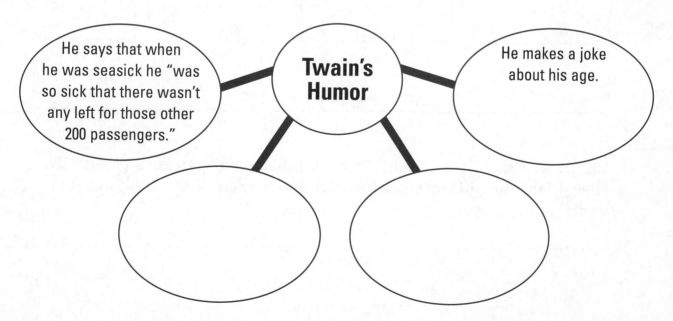

He says that when he was seasick he "was so sick that there wasn't any left for those other 200 passengers."

Twain's Humor

He makes a joke about his age.

Stage Fright

1. **Draw Conclusions:** Mark Twain was nervous before his first public speech. How would some stage fright help someone get ready to give a speech?

   _____

   _____

2. **Speculate:** Twain set up a signal with the governor's wife before his first speech. Then, he looked at her after he gave the sad "gem" in his speech. What probably happened when Twain looked at her?

   _____

   _____

3. **Reading Skill: Opinions** are what a person thinks or believes. Twain gives opinions in his speech. Use this chart to record two **opinions** that Twain gives. Then, list clue words that help you identify each opinion.

Opinion	Clue Word

4. **Literary Analysis:** "Stage Fright" is written from Mark Twain's perspective. How might the **author's perspective** be different if his daughter had written the essay?

   _____

   _____

SUPPORT FOR WRITING AND EXTEND YOUR LEARNING

Writing: Dramatic Scene

Write a **dramatic scene** using Twain's description of his first public appearance. Answer the following questions to help you write your dramatic scene.

- What might two audience members have talked about after Twain's first speech?

  _____

  _____

- What might Twain's daughter have said to him after his speech at her recital?

  _____

  _____

Listening and Speaking: Speech

Plan a **speech** on stage fright. Answer the following questions to help you write your speech about stage fright.

- Will your speech be better if it is funny or serious? Why?

  _____

  _____

- You want your audience to understand how stage fright feels. How can you do this?

  _____

  _____

My Papa, Mark Twain

Susy Clemens

Summary Thirteen-year-old Susy Clemens writes about her famous father, Mark Twain. Her kind descriptions of her father's looks, actions, and writing show how she feels about him.

Reading/Writing Connection

Complete each sentence to describe someone you admire.

1. To <u>identify</u> this person, I would say _____.

2. I would <u>focus</u> on his/her _____.

3. To <u>conclude</u>, I would say _____

_____.

Note-taking Guide

Use this chart to record Susy Clemens's thoughts and feelings about her father.

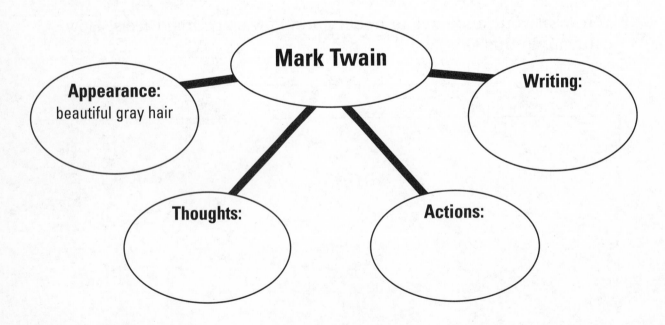

My Papa, Mark Twain
Susy Clemens

We are a very happy family. We <u>consist</u> of Papa, Mamma, Jean, Clara and me. It is papa I am writing about, and I shall have no trouble in not knowing what to say about him, as he is a *very* <u>striking</u> character.

♦ ♦ ♦

The author said that Papa had beautiful gray hair, an attractive nose, kind eyes, and a mustache. He was a very handsome and fit man. He was also a good man, and he was very funny. Sometimes he had a bad temper, but everyone in her family did. Sometimes he was forgetful. And sometimes, he paced back and forth across a room while he thought.

♦ ♦ ♦

Papa is very fond of animals <u>particularly</u> of cats, we had a dear little gray kitten once that he named "Lazy" (papa always wears gray to match his hair and eyes) and he would carry him around on his shoulder, it was a mighty pretty sight! the gray cat sound asleep against papa's gray coat and hair.

♦ ♦ ♦

The author's father gave the family cats very funny names, such as Stray Kit, Buffalo Bill, and Soapy Sall.

The author's father often used strong language, and he didn't like to be interrupted. He said that he didn't like to listen to anyone talk except himself. The author says he meant that as a joke, but she thinks there is some truth in it!

♦ ♦ ♦

Vocabulary Development

consist (kuhn SIST) *v.*   be made up of
striking (STRYK ing) *adj.*   interesting; noticeable
particularly (per TIK yuh ler lee) *adv.*   especially; more than others

TAKE NOTES

Activate Prior Knowledge

Think about someone you admire, or like a great deal. What do you like about this person?

_____

_____

Reading Skill

Facts can be proved to be true. **Opinions** are what a person believes. Write one fact found in the bracketed paragraph.

_____

_____

Build English Skills

A compound sentence is two sentences joined by a conjunction such as *and, but,* or *or.* A comma usually appears before the conjunction in a compound sentence. Underline a compound sentence in the second bracketed paragraph.

Reading Check

What color does Twain always wear?

_____

Circle the reason in the text.

Read the bracketed paragraph. Circle *enoyed.* Say the word aloud. What word does this sound like?

_____

Circle any other words that you think are misspelled.

Vocabulary and Pronunciation

The suffix *-ist* can mean "a person who does a certain duty or makes a specific thing." A *humorist* is a person who writes something that is funny. What does the following word mean?

cyclist _____

Literary Analysis

The author's **perspective** shows the writer's feelings and beliefs about a subject. How might this biography be different if some-one outside Mark Twain's family had written it?

_____

_____

Culture Note

The phrase to *play hookey* means "to skip, or not go to, school." It means the same as "cutting school."

One of papa's latest books is "The Prince and the Pauper" and it is unquestionably the best book he has ever written, some people want him to keep to his old style, some gentleman wrote him, "I enjoyed Huckleberry Finn immensely and am glad to see that you have returned to your old style." That enoyed me, that enoyed me greatly, because it trobles me to have so few people know papa, I mean realy know him, they think of Mark Twain as a humorist joking at everything . . . .

◆ ◆ ◆

The author said that people described him in the strangest ways. For example, they said that he had messy red hair and a wrinkled, sad face. The author said that it's not true. And he's not always funny. She wanted him to write a book that showed his soft, kind side. She thought "The Prince and the Pauper" did that perfectly.

◆ ◆ ◆

I never saw a man with so much variety of feeling as papa has; now the "Prince and the Pauper" is full of touching places, but there is always a streak of humor in them somewhere. Papa very <u>seldom</u> writes a passage without some humor in it somewhere and I don't think he ever will.

◆ ◆ ◆

When the author's father was young, he played "hookey" all the time. Sometimes he even pretended to be dying so that he would not have to go to school! Instead of making him go to school, his mother let him go to work in a printing office.

◆ ◆ ◆

He did so, and gradually picked up enough education to <u>enable</u> him to do about as well as those who were more studious in early life.

Vocabulary Development

seldom (SEL duhm) *adv.* not very often
enable (i NAY buhl) *v.* allow

My Papa, Mark Twain

1. **Deduce:** Susy's father often played tricks to get out of going to school. Explain how you think Susy feels about her father's lack of formal education.

   _____

   _____

2. **Speculate:** This essay contains many misspelled words. Why do you think the misspelled words were not corrected?

   _____

   _____

3. **Reading Skill:** Use this chart to list two **opinions** that Susy gives about her father. Then, list the clue words that helped you know that each one is an opinion.

Opinion	Clue Word

4. **Literary Analysis:** You can understand an **author's perspective** by finding out details about the author's life. List one detail from Susy Clemens's life that helps you see her author's perspective.

   _____

   _____

SUPPORT FOR WRITING AND EXTEND YOUR LEARNING

Writing: Dramatic Scene

Turn a passage from "My Papa, Mark Twain" into a **dramatic scene**. Answer the following questions to help you write your dramatic scene.

- First, you must choose a passage from the essay for your scene. Your passage should have at least two characters. What is your passage about?

  _____

  _____

- Which characters are speaking?

  _____

- How do the characters feel as they are talking?

  _____

Research and Technology: Research for Charts

Create a **poster** that shows some of Mark Twain's best-known works and characters. Use this chart to list details about the stories and characters you choose to put on your poster.

Title of Work	Important Character(s)	Description of Work	Description of Character(s)

The Lady and the Spider • Names/Nombres

READING SKILL

You should know the difference between **fact and opinion**. This will help you understand nonfiction writing.

- A *fact* can be proved.
- An *opinion* is a belief that can be supported but not proved.

You can **check facts by using resources** such as dictionaries, encyclopedias, and reliable Web sites.

Use this chart to keep track of facts in these selections.

Fact	Reference Source	True	False
Tigers live in only cold climates.	Internet		✓

LITERARY ANALYSIS

Writers have thoughts and feelings about the subject of and audience for their work. These thoughts and feelings are called **tone**.

- Tone can often be described in one word, such as *playful*, *serious*, and *humorous*.
- Word choice, sentence structure, and sentence length help create a tone.

Notice how word choice can create a friendly tone:

If you plan ahead, I promise that you'll have the best party ever!

As you read, look for details that show a certain tone.

The Lady and the Spider

Robert Fulghum

Summary The narrator sees his neighbor walk into a spider's web. She screams. The narrator writes about the event from the lady's point of view and from the spider's point of view.

Reading/Writing Connection

Complete each sentence to list reasons why a spider might be afraid of a human.

1. Spiders are afraid to <u>capture</u> humans because _____.

2. Spiders are afraid to <u>confront</u> humans because _____.

3. A human might <u>injure</u> a spider by _____.

Note-taking Guide

Use this chart to record each character's reaction to the neighbor's walking into the spider web.

The Lady	The Spider	The Narrator
She screams.		

The Lady and the Spider

1. **Infer:** The lady walks into the spider web. She throws her bags. What does her action show about her feelings toward spiders?

   _____

   _____

2. **Analyze:** The narrator tells the lady's and spider's thoughts. Why do you think the narrator tells what they both are thinking?

   _____

   _____

3. **Reading Skill:** Suppose that you must prove two facts from this essay. You will use the Internet. What two **facts** will you prove?

   _____

   _____

4. **Literary Analysis:** The passage in this chart has an informal **tone**. _Informal_ means "friendly." Rewrite this passage. Use a formal tone. _Formal_ means "serious." Write in the space provided.

Informal Tone	Formal Tone
Spiders. Amazing creatures. Been around maybe 350 million years, so they can cope with just about anything. Lots of them, too—sixty or seventy thousand per suburban acre. It's the web thing that I envy.	

SUPPORT FOR WRITING AND EXTEND YOUR LEARNING

Writing: Personal Anecdote

Write a **personal anecdote** about your encounter with something in nature. First, choose the experience you plan to write about. Answer the following questions to help you write your anecdote.

- Where does the story take place? _____

  _____

- When does the story take place? _____

  _____

- Who is in the story? _____

  _____

- What is the most important event in the story? _____

  _____

Listening and Speaking: Monologue

A **monologue** is a speech in which one person tells about himself or herself. Choose either the lady or the spider. Write a monologue that presents the thoughts of the character that you chose.

- What adjectives will you use to describe the feelings of the lady or the spider?

  _____

  _____

- Explain what the lady thinks about spiders in general, or explain what the spider thinks about humans in general.

  _____

  _____

- How did the meeting of the lady and the spider affect the rest of the lady's or the spider's day?

  _____

  _____

HELLO
my name is

Julia

Names/Nombres

Julia Alvarez

Summary Young Julia Alvarez and her family are called by different names when they come to America. The names are not the Spanish names they use at home. Julia wonders what name she will use when she becomes a well-known writer.

Reading/Writing Connection

Complete each sentence to describe what is good about belonging to a group.

1. Each person in a group can <u>contribute</u> _____.

2. In a group, people can <u>identify</u> with _____.

3. People like to <u>participate</u> in a group because _____.

Note-taking Guide

Julia Alvarez describes names in this essay. Her name is mispronounced. Her friends call her names other than Julia. She also has nicknames. Use this chart to list the different names or pronunciations of names in Alvarez's essay.

What people call her father	What people call her mother	What people call Julia
Mister Elbures, Mister Alberase		

Think of a time when you joined a new team or group. Maybe you moved to a new neighborhood or school. What did it feel like to be the new person?

_____

_____

A **fact** can be proved. An **opinion** can be supported but not proved. Read the bracketed paragraph. What **fact** does Julia Alvarez state?

_____

_____

The family's last name is mispronounced when they arrive in New York City. Circle the names that Alvarez hears.

In the Spanish language, the letter _j_ is usually pronounced as an _h_ is pronounced in English. Circle how Alvarez writes her name should be pronounced.

Names/Nombres
Julia Alvarez

Have you ever been in a situation where you felt like an outsider? What were you willing to do so that you would seem to be more like everyone else? In "Names/Nombres," Julia, the narrator, tells how she lets others call her by different names so she will seem more American. She doesn't like being asked where she is from, and she doesn't like being asked to say her name in Spanish.

As the essay begins, Julia tells what happens to her family name, Alvarez, when she arrives in New York City:

◆　◆　◆

When we arrived in New York City, our names changed almost immediately. At immigration,[1] the officer asked my father, _Mister Elbures_, if he had anything to declare.

◆　◆　◆

Julia's father simply answers the question, but Julia is bothered that the immigration officer cannot pronounce her family's last name. She is afraid to correct him. She says their name over and over to herself and thinks it has a beautiful sound.

◆　◆　◆

When we moved into our new apartment building, the super[2] called my father _Mister Alberase_, and the neighbors who became mother's friends pronounced her name _Jew-lee-ah_ instead of _Hoo-lee-ah_. I, her <u>namesake</u>, was known as

---

Vocabulary Development

namesake (NAYM sayk) _n._   a person of the same name

---

1. **Immigration** (im uh GRAY shuhn) _n._ government agency that processes immigrants.
2. **super** (SOO per) _n._ superintendent; the person who manages an apartment building.

Hoo-lee-tah at home. But at school, I was *Judy*, or *Judith*, and once an English teacher mistook me for *Juliet*.

It took awhile to get used to my new names. I wondered if I shouldn't correct my teachers and new friends. But my mother argued that it didn't matter. "You know what your friend Shakespeare said, '*A rose by any other name would smell as sweet.*'" My father had gotten into the habit of calling any famous author "my friend" because I had begun to write poems and stories in English class.

◆ ◆ ◆

In high school, Julia is popular with the other students. They call her Jules or Hey Jude. Some kids call her Alcatraz.[3] Julia imagines that such a name will allow her to cause trouble. And when JUDY ALCATRAZ appears on wanted posters, nobody will ever trace the name to her.

Julia's older sister *Mauricia* has the most foreign-sounding name. *Mauricia* is a combination of *Mauran* and *Felicia*, the names of both of her grandmothers. Americans seem to have trouble pronouncing *Mao-ree-shee-ah*. They even have trouble with *Moor-ee-sha*, so they call her *Maria* or Marsha or Maudy from her nickname *Maury*. Julia's little sister, *Ana*, has the easiest time with her name. People call her *Anne*.

Julia is happy to be Judy and merge with the Sallys and Janes in her class. But her accent and coloring give her away. When her classmates ask her where she is from, she tells them the Dominican Republic.

◆ ◆ ◆

3. **Alcatraz** Alcatraz is an island in San Francisco Bay in northern California. It was the site of a federal prison for dangerous criminals.

TAKE NOTES

Literary Analysis

Tone shows the writer's attitude or feelings abut the audience and subject. Read the underlined sentences. How would you describe Alvarez's **tone** or attitude toward people who do not call her Julia?

_____

Word choice can show the **tone** of a piece. Draw a box around the word in this passage that supports your answer.

Stop to Reflect

Alvarez's mother is saying a line from Act II of Shakespeare's play *Romeo and Juliet:* "That which we call a rose/By any other name would smell as sweet." What do you think this sentence means?

_____

Culture Note

Lisa, Mary, and Susan were the most popular girls' names in the 1960s. The names Emily, Madison, and Hannah were the most popular names in the United States from 2000 to 2004. What names are popular in your home country?

Alvarez's essay has a humorous, friendly **tone** so far. Read the first bracketed paragraph. Alvarez's classmates ask her where she is from. She describes how their curiosity makes her feel. Has the **tone** of the essay changed? Explain.

_____

_____

Read the second bracketed passage. Alvarez gives her full name in this passage. Why is her name so long?

_____

_____

Is this a **fact** or an **opinion**?

_____

What **opinion** does Alvarez have of her full, Spanish name?

_____

_____

The word _too_ can mean "very" or "overly." It can also mean "also." What meaning do you think _too_ has in the underlined sentence?

_____

They were just being curious, I knew, but I burned with shame whenever they singled me out as a "foreigner," a rare, exotic friend.

◆ ◆ ◆

Once Julia shocks her classmates by reciting her entire name. It includes many family names that go back generations. Her classmates beg her to say it again.

◆ ◆ ◆

"Julia Altagracia Maria Teresa Álvarez Tavares Perello Espaillat Julia Pérez Rochet González," I pronounced it slowly, a name as chaotic with sounds as a Middle Eastern bazaar[4] or market day in a South American village.

◆ ◆ ◆

Julia's large extended family, many aunts, uncles, and cousins, come to Julia's high school graduation. Introducing them to her friends is difficult. There are so many of them and their names are so complicated. Julia's friends rarely have more than a "Mom and Dad" to introduce. Julia and her friends sign yearbooks with nicknames such as "Beans" and "Pepperoni" and "Alcatraz." They hug each other, cry, and promise to keep in touch.

◆ ◆ ◆

Our goodbyes went on too long. I heard my father's voice calling out across the parking lot, "_Hoo-lee-tah! Vamonos!_"

◆ ◆ ◆

After graduation, Julia's family has a party for her at home. Her family, including tíos, tías, primas, her parents, and hermanas, is

---

Vocabulary Development

vamonos (VAH moh nohs) _v._   Spanish for "Let's go"

---

4. **bazaar** (buh ZAHR) _n._ marketplace; frequently one held outdoors.

all there. They all enjoy Spanish food and a special dessert, inscribed Happy Graduation Julia. She gets many presents, including jewelry and money.

◆ ◆ ◆

The biggest gift was a portable typewriter from my parents for writing my stories and poems. Someday, the family predicted, my name would be well-known throughout the United States. I laughed to myself, wondering which one I would go by.

TAKE NOTES

Reading Skill

Read the bracketed paragraph. What **opinion** does Alvarez's family have about her future?

_____

_____

Underline the words that help you know that this is an **opinion**.

Literary Analysis

Read the last sentence in the essay. What is the **tone** of the sentence? Explain.

_____

_____

Vocabulary and Pronunciation

The word *dessert* means "a sweet food served at the end of a meal." It is pronounced di ZUHRT. A *desert* means "an area of dry land." It is pronounced DI zuhrt. Name your favorite *dessert*. Then, name a *desert*.

_____

_____

Reading Check

Circle the gift that would be most useful for a writer.

Names/Nombres

1. **Draw Conclusions:** Why is Julia embarrassed when her classmates ask her where she is from?

_____

_____

2. **Analyze:** How do Julia's feelings about her name change over time?

_____

_____

3. **Reading Skill:** Alvarez tells the story of her graduation by writing, "Our goodbyes went on too long." Is this a **fact** or an **opinion**? Explain.

_____

_____

4. **Literary Analysis:** "Names/Nombres" is written in an informal, or friendly, **tone**. Use this chart to rewrite the two sentences in a more serious, or formal, tone.

Informal Tone	Formal Tone
"It took a while to get used to my new names."	
"My mother blushed and admitted her baby's real name to the group."	

SUPPORT FOR WRITING AND EXTEND YOUR LEARNING

Writing: Personal Anecdote

Write a **personal anecdote** about your family. First, choose the experience you plan to write about. Answer the following questions to help you write your anecdote.

- Where does the story take place? _____

_____

- When does the story take place? _____

_____

- Who is in the story? _____

_____

- What is the most important event in the story? _____

_____

_____

Research and Technology: Presentation

Your **presentation** about the Dominican Republic will include plenty of information. Use this chart to record the order of events that contributed to Julia Alvarez's family's leaving the Dominican Republic.

1950–1954	1955–1959	1960–1964	1965–1979

Atlas

ABOUT ATLASES

An **atlas** is a book of maps. The maps show cities, mountains, rivers, and roads. Some atlases also have facts or short articles about the places on the maps. Atlas maps usually have the following:

- a *compass rose* that shows north, south, east, and west
- a *scale bar* that shows how many miles or kilometers are in one inch on the map
- a *legend* or key that explains the symbols and colors on the map
- *labels* that have the names and locations of places
- an *inset map* that shows where a location can be found on the globe

READING SKILL

A **generalization** is a broad statement based on many examples. Generalizations are true if they are supported by facts. Generalizations are faulty, or false, if they are not supported by facts. For example, "Dogs are dangerous" is a generalization. This statement includes all dogs. However, not all dogs are dangerous. This would be a false generalization.

The information in an atlas entry can help you **make generalizations** about a place. Use this checklist to help you make generalizations based on facts in an atlas:

Using an Atlas to Make Generalizations

❏ Use the compass rose to support generalizations about locations.

❏ Use the scale bar to support generalizations about distances.

❏ Use the key to support generalizations about such subjects as the size of cities and the height of mountains.

The Caribbean

The Caribbean Sea is enclosed by an arc of many hundreds of islands, islets, and offshore reefs that reach from Florida, in the US, round to Venezuela in South America. From 1492, Spain, France, Britain, and the Netherlands claimed the islands as colonies.

LAND HEIGHT

- 6,560–13,120ft
- 3,280–6,560ft
- 1,640–3,280ft
- 820–1,640ft
- 330–820ft
- 0–330ft

SEA DEPTH

- 0–820ft
- 820–1,640ft
- 1,640–3,280ft
- 3,280–6,560ft
- 6,560–9,840ft
- 9,840–13,120ft
- Below 13,120ft

CITIES AND TOWNS

- Over 500,000 people
- 100,000–500,000
- 50,000–100,000
- Less than 50,000

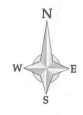

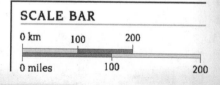

SCALE BAR

| 0 km | 100 | 200 |

| 0 miles | 100 | 200 |

THE LANDSCAPE

The islands are formed from two main mountain chains: the Greater Antilles, which are part of a chain running from west to east, and the Lesser Antilles, which run from north to south. The mountains are now almost submerged under the Atlantic Ocean and Caribbean Sea. Only the higher peaks reach above sea level to form islands.

The Bahamas

The Bahamas are low-lying islands formed from limestone rock. Their coastlines are fringed by coral reefs, lagoons, and mangrove swamps. Some of the bigger islands are covered with forests.

Hispaniola

Two countries, Haiti and the Dominican Republic, occupy the island of Hispaniola. The land is mostly mountainous, broken by fertile valleys.

Cuba

Cuba is the largest island in the Antilles. Its landscape is made up of wide, fertile plains with rugged hills and mountains in the southeast.

The Lesser Antilles

Most of these small volcanic islands have mountainous interiors. Barbados and Antigua are flatter, with some higher volcanic areas. Montserrat was evacuated in 1997, following volcanic eruptions on the island.

FARMING AND LAND USE

Agriculture is an important source of income, with over half of all produce exported. Many islands have fertile, well-watered land and large areas set aside for commercial crops such as sugarcane, tobacco, and coffee. Some islands rely heavily on a single crop; in Dominica, bananas provide over half the country's income. Cuba is one of the world's biggest sugar producers.

FARMING
AND LAND USE

🐂 Cattle
🐟 Fishing
🐖 Pigs
🦃 Poultry
🦐 Shellfish
🍌 Bananas
☕ Coffee
🌾 Sugarcane
🌿 Tobacco

■ Cropland
■ Forest
■ Pasture
• Major conurbation

THINKING ABOUT THE ATLAS

1. Which Caribbean islands are not mountainous?

   _____

2. Compare the "Landscape" map with the "Farming and Land Use" map. Which map contains more details? Describe the types of details the map shows.

   _____

READING SKILL

3. Is the generalization "All of the mountains are in a chain that runs east to west" true or false? Explain.

   _____

4. Is the generalization "At least half of the land on the islands shown is used for pastures and crops" true or false? Explain.

   _____

TIMED WRITING: DESCRIPTION (20 minutes)

Find the city of Havana, Cuba, on the Farming and Land Use map. Write a description of the island of Cuba. Use the facts presented in the atlas to make generalizations. Answer these questions to help you write your generalizations.

- What kinds of food are grown on Cuba?

  _____

- What kinds of animals are raised on Cuba?

  _____

- What are the waters surrounding the island used for?

  _____

EASILY CONFUSED WORDS

Some words that you use often are easy to confuse with each other. They may sound almost the same or have similar spellings

Do You Know now? Like the words on the list, *know* and *now* are easily confused. You most likely know the difference between words like these. In writing, though, you may forget and choose the wrong one. In addition, homonyms and homophones sound the same but are spelled differently. The spell checker in a word processing program will not find this kind of error, so proofread carefully.

Word List
our
are
than
then
know
now
lose
loose
accept
except

Practice Read the following paragraph. Circle any word that is misspelled. Then, write the misspelled word correctly on the blank.

Are teacher gave us an essay to write for homework. Everyone accept Jason was excited about the assignment. The teacher told us that we would loose points if we did not turn the essay in on time. Jason said that he did not now what to write about. Our teacher gave him some ideas. Than, he was happier.

_____

_____

_____

_____

The Wounded Wolf

A **short story** is a short, made-up story. A short story has a plot, characters, a setting, and a theme. **Plot** is the action in the story. All plots have these features:

- a series of events. A plot's events are connected by causes and effects.

- a **conflict**, or struggle.

- a high point called the **climax**.

- a **resolution**, the part of the story in which the problem is solved. The resolution comes after the climax.

Conflict
A problem between two opposing forces

Internal	External
• Takes place inside a character • Character struggles to make decision, take action, or overcome problem • **Example:** A character cannot decide whether to save money or buy something he or she wants.	• Takes place outside a character • Character struggles with an outside force such as another character or nature • **Example:** A character gets caught outside in a snowstorm.

Characters are the people or animals who take part in the action of the story.

- **Characterization:** An author uses characterization to create and develop a character.

- **Character's traits:** All characters have traits, or qualities. These traits help readers understand why the characters act the way they do.

- **Character's motives:** A character's motives are the reasons why he or she does something.

Setting is the time and place of a story's action. The setting's details can include the year, the time of day, and the weather.

The setting can be important to the plot. The setting can also help set the story's mood.

- Details that seem real are included in stories that take place in recent times.

- Real and made-up details are usually included in stories that take place in the past.

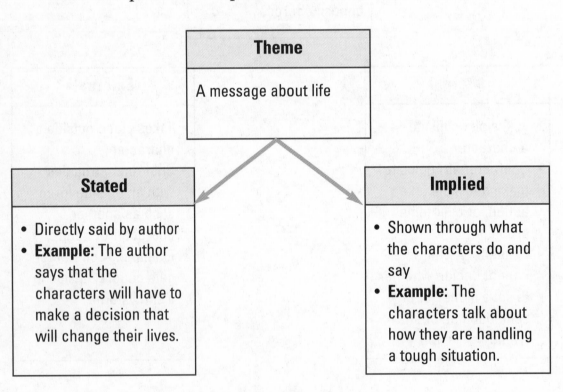

Theme

A message about life

Stated

- Directly said by author
- **Example:** The author says that the characters will have to make a decision that will change their lives.

Implied

- Shown through what the characters do and say
- **Example:** The characters talk about how they are handling a tough situation.

The Wounded Wolf

Jean Craighead George

Summary Roko the wolf gets hurt while fighting for food. Hungry animals that prey on dying animals follow him. Roko finds shelter under a rock. The hungry animals wait nearby. The lead wolf from Roko's pack finds Roko. All of the animals wait to see whether Roko will get better or die under the rock.

Note-taking Guide

Many animals watch Roko after he is injured. Use this chart to record what the animals do.

Ravens	White Fox	Snowy Owl	Grizzly Bear	Kiglo
Pick Roko's open wound				

What have you heard or read about wolves? Give two details below.

_____

_____

Build English Skills

A compound verb names two or more actions done by the same subject. For example, they *laugh* and *sing*. Underline two sentences in the bracketed paragraph that contain compound verbs.

Short Story

An **external conflict** is a struggle between a character and something outside that character, such as another character or nature. What is Roko's conflict at the start of the story?

_____

_____

_____

Reading Check

Underline the name of Kiglo's pack.

The Wounded Wolf
Jean Craighead George

A wounded wolf climbs Toklat Ridge, a <u>massive</u> spine of rock and ice. As he limps, dawn strikes the ridge and lights it up with sparks and stars. Roko, the wounded wolf, blinks in the ice fire, then stops to rest and watch his pack run the thawing Arctic valley.

They plunge and turn. They fight the mighty caribou that struck young Roko with his hoof and wounded him. He jumped between the beast and Kiglo, leader of the Toklat pack. Young Roko spun and fell. Hooves, paws, and teeth roared over him. And then his pack and the beast were gone.

<u>Gravely</u> injured, Roko pulls himself toward the shelter rock. Weakness overcomes him. He stops. He and his pack are thin and hungry. This is the season of starvation. . . .

Young Roko glances down the valley. He droops his head and stiffens his tail to signal to his pack that he is badly hurt. Winds <u>wail</u>. A frigid blast picks up long <u>shawls</u> of snow and drapes them between young Roko and his pack. And so his message is not read.

◆   ◆   ◆

A nearby raven sees Roko's signal and calls out that something is dying. Soon Roko is followed by a group of hungry ravens.

◆   ◆   ◆

Roko snarls and hurries toward the shelter rock. A cloud of snow envelops him. He limps in blinding whiteness now.

Vocabulary Development

massive (MAS iv) *adj.*   huge; large and impressive
gravely (GRAYV lee) *adv.*   badly
wail (wayl) *v.*   make a loud crying sound
shawls (shawlz) *n.*   capelike cloths

A ghostly presence flits around. "Hahahahahahaha," the white fox states—death is coming to the Ridge. Roko smells the fox tagging at his heels.

The cloud whirls off. Two golden eyes look up at Roko. The snowy owl has heard the ravens and joined the deathwatch.

◆　◆　◆

The ravens, fox, and owl are joined by a grizzly bear. The animals follow Roko as he struggles up Toklat Ridge. As Roko becomes weaker, the other animals grow bold and move in closer.

◆　◆　◆

Roko stops; his breath comes hard. A raven alights upon his back and picks the open wound. Roko snaps. The raven flies and circles back. The white fox nips at Roko's toes. The snowy owl inches closer. The grizzly bear, still dulled by sleep, stumbles onto Toklat Ridge.

Only yards from the shelter rock, Roko falls. Instantly the ravens mob him. They scream and peck and stab at his eyes. The white fox leaps upon his wound. The snowy owl sits and waits.

Young Roko struggles to his feet. He bites the ravens. Snaps the fox. And lunges at the stoic owl. He turns and warns the grizzly bear. Then he bursts into a run and falls against the shelter rock. The wounded wolf wedges down between the rock and barren ground. Now protected on three sides, he turns and faces all his foes.

The ravens step a few feet closer. The fox slides toward him on his belly. The snowy owl blinks and waits, and on the ridge rim roars the hungry grizzly bear.

Vocabulary Development

alights (uh LYTS) *v.*   lands
stoic (STO ik) *adj.*   showing no reaction to good or bad events; calm and unaffected by hardship
barren (BAR en) *adj.*   empty

TAKE NOTES

Short Story

The **conflict** is growing in the story. Read the bracketed paragraph. What is the **internal conflict** that Roko faces?

_____

Read Fluently

A **dependent clause** is a group of words that has a subject and a verb. Dependent clauses that begin sentences usually start with the words *as, because,* or *even though.* Underline the dependent clause that comes at the beginning of a sentence in the second bracketed paragraph.

Short Story

A **character's motives** are the reasons for his or her actions. Why are the animals following Roko?

_____

_____

Short Story

The **theme** of a story can be found by noticing how a character deals with a situation. How does Roko react to the ravens, fox, and owl?

_____

Vocabulary and Pronunciation

Read the first bracketed paragraph. Sometimes writers explain a word in the sentence after the word is first used. Underline the words that help you figure out the meaning of *roll call*. Write its meaning.

_____

Short Story

The **climax** is the high point of a story, when the end of the story becomes clear. Read the second bracketed passage. What is becoming clear about Roko?

_____

Short Story

Characterization is the way that the author develops characters. What does Kiglo do to Roko's nose?

_____

Underline the words that tell the meaning of the gesture.

Reading Check

What happens as the grizzly leaves? Circle the answer.

Roko growls.

The sun comes up. Far across the Toklat Valley, Roko hears his pack's "hunt's end" song. The music wails and sobs, wilder than the bleating wind. The hunt song ends. Next comes the roll call. Each member of the Toklat pack barks to say that he is home and well.

"Kiglo here," Roko hears his leader bark. There is a pause. It is young Roko's turn. He cannot lift his head to answer. The pack is silent. The leader starts the count once more. "Kiglo here."—A pause. Roko cannot answer.

◆　◆　◆

Soon Kiglo hears the ravens' death song. He knows that Roko is dying.

◆　◆　◆

The hours pass. The wind slams snow on Toklat Ridge. Massive clouds blot out the sun. In their gloom Roko sees the deathwatch move in closer. Suddenly he hears the musk-oxen thundering into their circle. The ice cracks as the grizzly leaves. The ravens burst into the air. The white fox runs. The snowy owl flaps to the top of the shelter rock. And Kiglo rounds the knoll.

In his mouth he carries meat. He drops it close to Roko's head and wags his tail excitedly. Roko licks Kiglo's chin to honor him. Then Kiglo puts his mouth around Roko's nose. This gesture says "I am your leader." . . .

The wounded wolf wags his tail. Kiglo trots away.

Already Roko's wound feels better. . . .

◆　◆　◆

Kiglo continues to bring food to Roko. Each day, Roko grows stronger.

◆　◆　◆

One dawn he moves his wounded leg. He stretches it and pulls himself into the sunlight.

Vocabulary Development
knoll (nohl) *n.*　hill

He walks—he romps. He runs in circles. He leaps and plays with chunks of ice. Suddenly he stops. The "hunt's end" song rings out. Next comes the roll call.

"Kiglo here."

"Roko here," he barks out strongly.

The pack is silent.

"Kiglo here," the leader repeats.

"Roko here."

Across the distance comes the sound of whoops and yipes and barks and howls. They fill the dawn with celebration. And Roko prances down the Ridge.

TAKE NOTES

Short Story

The **plot** of a short story has a **resolution**. This is the part of the story that tells how the problem is solved. How is Roko's problem solved?

_____

_____

_____

Culture Note

Some people raise dogs that are part wolf. Some people think that this is a dangerous animal to have. What animals in your native country do some people think are too dangerous to have as pets?

_____

_____

_____

Stop to Reflect

Why do you think Kiglo repeats his roll call?

_____

_____

_____

Reading Check

What call comes before the roll call? Underline the answer.

Short Stories

1. **Analyze:** What does Roko do to try to save himself?

   _____

   _____

2. **Infer:** Wolves live in packs. Kiglo tries to help Roko, his packmate. What does Kiglo's behavior show about how wolves take care of pack members?

   _____

   _____

3. The **conflict** is the problem a character faces. What is the main conflict in "The Wounded Wolf"? Explain.

   _____

   _____

4. The **setting** is where and when a story takes place. Fill in the chart below to describe the setting of the story. Write a detail in the first column that helps you picture the setting. Then, tell what that detail means to the struggle for survival. Finally, explain in the third column why the setting is important to the story.

What It Says	What It Means	Why It Is Important

RESEARCH THE AUTHOR

Plan for a Multimedia Presentation

- Jean Craighead George has written many books about animals and people surviving in the wild. She has also written a series on wolves. *Julie of the Wolves*, *Julie*, and *Julie's Wolf Pack* came out of the author's trip to Denali National Park in Alaska.

- Search the Internet for words and phrases such as "Jean Craighead George" or "Jean Craighead George books." Search the author's Web site for information about her writing: www.jeancraigheadgeorge.com/
  What I learned:

  _____

  _____

  _____

- Search the library and the Internet for photographs of the author. You might even find photographs or drawings of her subjects.

- Search through Jean Craighead George's books to find the two or three that you like the most. Write a summary for each book by including the most important information. Add this information to your report for your presentation.

- Watch the video interview with Jean Craighead George, and review your source material. Use this information to answer the following questions.

1. What did you learn about Craighead George's life that is interesting?

   _____

2. How has the author's interest in the natural world influenced her books?

   _____

The Tail • Dragon, Dragon

READING SKILL

You **make inferences** when you make guesses about what is not directly said. You do this by using **details** in the story. Look at the examples in this sentence:

Example: Arnie *ran* to the mailbox to see whether Jim's letter had *finally* arrived.

The word *finally* tells you that Arnie has been waiting a long time. You can guess, or infer, that Arnie has been waiting to hear from Jim. You can infer from *ran* that Arnie is eager to get the letter.

LITERARY ANALYSIS

Characterization is the way that writers describe characters. You learn about a character's qualities and personality, such as whether the character is friendly or mean.

- With **direct characterization**, writers make statements about a character.

- With **indirect characterization**, writers show a character's thoughts, words, and actions. Writers also use indirect characterization to show what other characters say and think about a certain character.

Use this graphic organizer to keep track of details that show what each character is like.

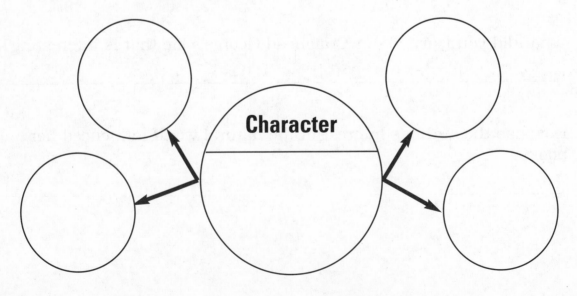

The Tail

Joyce Hansen

Summary Tasha is upset. She has to babysit all summer for her seven-year-old brother, Junior. Their mother gives rules for Tasha and Junior to follow. Junior plays a trick on his sister. The trick teaches Tasha how important it is to obey her mother's rules.

Reading/Writing Connection

Complete each sentence to show why babysitting for a brother or sister can be difficult.

1. It is hard to <u>enforce</u> _____ with a little sister.

2. Siblings always want to <u>accompany</u> big sisters to _____.

3. A baby-sitter must not <u>consent</u> to _____.

Note-taking Guide

Fill in this chart with details about the events in "The Tail." List one unexpected thing that happens to each character in the story.

Tasha	Junior	Naomi	Mother	Dog
She has to babysit for her brother all summer.				

The Tail
Joyce Hansen

School was ending for the year, and Tasha was looking forward to summer vacation. But as she was washing the last supper dish, her mother gave her the bad news. Ma was going back to her job. And, because Tasha was thirteen, her mother thought it was time for her to help out with family responsibilities. Ma wanted her to spend each summer day watching Junior. Suddenly it looked like the worst summer of Tasha's life.

◆　◆　◆

"Oh, no!" I broke the dish with a crash. "Not that, Mama." Junior is my seven-year-old brother and has been following me like a tail ever since he learned how to walk. And to make matters worse, there are no kids Junior's age on our block. Everyone is either older or younger than he is.

◆　◆　◆

But Ma had made up her mind. Before she left for work the next morning, she set out the rules—lots of them. Tasha couldn't leave the block. She couldn't have any company, not even her best friend Naomi. She wasn't allowed to let Junior hike in the park, and she had to make him lunch. Ma would call at lunchtime to make sure they were eating. Then Ma told Junior to behave himself. Of course, he promised that he'd do whatever Tasha said.

Ma left, and Junior started bothering Tasha. Then her friend Naomi called. Tasha told Junior to grab his comic books and checkers game. Then they ran down the stairs of their apartment building and met Naomi, who was sitting on the front steps.

◆　◆　◆

"You ready for double-dutch practice?" she asked. "Yvonne and Keisha are going to meet us in the playground."

"Mama said we have to stay on the block," Junior answered before I could even open my mouth.

"No one's talking to you, Junior." I pulled Naomi up off the stoop. "I promised my mother we'd stay on the block, but the playground is just across the street. I can see the block from there."

"It's still not the block," Junior mumbled as we raced across the street.

◆　◆　◆

The playground where they jumped rope was near the entrance to the park. Tasha really wanted to go. Ma had said not to leave the block, but after all, they weren't going very far. Tasha promised Junior that she would do him a favor if he didn't tell Ma.

◆　◆　◆

Keisha and Yvonne turned and Naomi and I jumped together, practicing a new routine. We were so good that some of the boys in the stickball game watched us. A few elderly people stopped to look at us too. We had an audience, so I really showed off—spinning and doing a lot of fancy footwork.

Suddenly Junior jumped in the ropes with us and people laughed and clapped.

"Junior!" I screamed. "Get out of here!"

"Remember, your job is to watch me." He grinned. My foot slipped and all three of us got tangled in the ropes and fell.

"Your feet are too big!" Junior yelled.

Everybody roared. I was too embarrassed. I tried to grab him, but he got away from me.

Vocabulary Development

routine (roo TEEN) *n.*   a part of a work out or performance

---

TAKE NOTES

Culture Note

"Double-dutch" is a game played with jump ropes. Two ropes are turned in opposite directions while one or more people jump both of them. What games are popular in your native country?

_____

_____

Reading Skill

Read the bracketed paragraph. What can you **infer** are Tasha's feelings as the girls jump?

_____

_____

_____

Vocabulary and Pronunciation

The word *roar* is most often used to describe the noise a big animal, such as a lion, makes. The word *roared* is used here to mean "laugh long and loud." The word *embarrassed* means "very uncomfortable." Underline the words that tell why people were laughing at Tasha, her brother, and her friends.

What details in the bracketed passage can you use to **infer** that Tasha is not worried about the wild dogs?

_____

_____

_____

_____

Prefixes come at the beginning of words. They can be used to change the meaning of the original word. Circle the word in the underlined sentence that has a prefix that means "not." Write another word that you know that uses the same prefix.

_____

How does Tasha feel when she finds Junior's comic book?

_____

_____

_____

Underline the sentence that uses **indirect characterization** to show how she feels.

"Get lost," I hollered after him as he ran toward the swings.

I tried to forget how stupid I must've looked and went back to the ropes. I don't know how long we'd been jumping when suddenly a little kid ran by us yelling, "There's a wild dog loose up there!" He pointed to the steps that led deep inside the park.

◆　◆　◆

For a long time, people had claimed that wild dogs lived in the park, but no one had ever seen one. So Tasha and Naomi kept jumping. Then they noticed that kids were leaving. They were scared of the dogs. Suddenly Tasha realized that Junior was missing. She shouted for him, but there was no answer. The girls dashed all over the neighborhood, looking for Junior and calling him. Now Tasha was getting really scared.

The girls went back to the playground. Then Tasha ran on to the entrance of the park. Naomi told her not to go in there because the wild dogs might get her.

◆　◆　◆

I turned around. "If you're scared, don't come. Junior's my only baby brother. Dear God," I said out loud, "please let me find him. I will play any kind of game he wants. I'll never yell at him again. I promise never to be mean to him again in my life!"

◆　◆　◆

Naomi went with Tasha. Every time they heard a noise, they jumped. Tasha kept calling for Junior and getting more and more scared. Then the girls thought they saw a huge animal, like a bear or something, ahead on the path. The girls screamed, but it turned out to be just a dead tree trunk. However, next to it, Tasha saw one of Junior's comic books. She started to cry. What if a wild dog had torn him apart?

◆　◆　◆

Suddenly, there was an unbelievable growl. My legs turned to air as I flew down the steps. Naomi was ahead of me. Her two braids stuck out like propellers. My feet didn't even touch the ground. We screamed all the way down the steps. I tripped on the last step and was sprawled out on the ground. Two women passing by bent over me. "Child, are you hurt?" one of them asked.

Then I heard a familiar laugh above me and looked up into Junior's dimpled face. He laughed so hard, he held his stomach with one hand. His checkers game was in the other. A little tan, mangy dog stood next to him, wagging its tail.

◆ ◆ ◆

Tasha was angry, but Junior just kept laughing, and the little dog growled at Tasha. Then Junior said something that really made her mad.

◆ ◆ ◆

"Me and Thunder hid in the bushes. We followed you." He continued laughing. Then he turned to the dog. "Thunder, didn't Tasha look funny holding that stick like she was going to beat up the tree trunk?"

I put my hands around Junior's neck. "This is the end of the tail," I said.

Junior grinned. "You promised. 'I'll play any game he wants. I'll never yell at him again. I promise never to be mean to him again in my life.' "

◆ ◆ ◆

Naomi started laughing too, because the dog was so little. Was this the animal that everyone was afraid of? Junior said that

Vocabulary Development

propellers (pruh PEL erz) *n.*   pieces of equipment that spin around to make a ship or an airplane move
mangy (MAYN jee) *adj.*   having a skin condition that makes animals lose fur

TAKE NOTES

Build English Skills

Tasha says that her "legs turned to air" as she "flew down the stairs." Tasha's legs did not really turn into air. She also did not really fly. She means that she ran so fast that it seemed like her legs barely touched the ground. Now, use "flew" in a sentence.

_____

_____

_____

Literary Analysis

What does Junior's reaction in the bracketed passage show about his character?

_____

_____

_____

Is this **direct** or **indirect characterization**? Explain.

_____

_____

_____

Reading Check

What does Junior remind Tasha that she promised to do? Circle the answer.

How does Tasha's **character** change by the end of the story?

_____

_____

_____

_____

_____

Does Junior tell their mother about the incident in the park? Underline the text that supports your answer.

Thunder was his trusted guard. He wasn't wild; he just needed a friend. Then Tasha checked her watch and saw that it was almost time for Ma to call them at the apartment. They raced home, and Thunder followed them. The phone rang, and it was Ma. Tasha told her that everything was just fine.

◆　◆　◆

Well, the summer didn't turn out to be so terrible after all. My parents got Thunder cleaned up and let Junior keep him for a pet.

◆　◆　◆

Tasha didn't leave the block again. She and Naomi practiced double-dutch jumping on the sidewalk in front of the apartment building. Tasha played with Junior too. He wasn't such a pest any more, thanks to Thunder.

◆　◆　◆

. . . We won the double-dutch contest. And Junior never told my parents that I'd lost him. I found out that you never miss a tail until you almost lose it.

The Tail

1. **Analyze Cause and Effect:** What happens that makes Junior disappear?

   _____

2. **Interpret:** Tasha calls Junior a "tail." Later she says, "I found out that you never miss a tail until you almost lose one." What does Tasha mean by this?

   _____

3. **Reading Skill:** You use details in a story to **make inferences**, or guesses. Use this chart to list details that helped you make an inference about Tasha. One example is provided. Give one more example.

Details	Inference
Tasha tells Naomi, "If you're scared, don't come. Junior's my only baby brother."	Tasha is worried. She is determined to find Junior, with or without Naomi's help.

4. **Literary Analysis: Direct characterization** is what a writer says about a character. List two examples of direct characterization from the story.

   _____

   _____

SUPPORT FOR WRITING AND EXTEND YOUR LEARNING

Writing: Help-Wanted Advertisement

Write a **help-wanted ad** for a babysitter. Answer the following questions to help you organize information for your ad.

- What would you give a babysitter in return for his or her services?

  _____

- What kind of on-the-job training might you provide?

  _____

- What information is usually at the top of an ad?

  _____

- What information needs to be in large or bold print?

  _____

Research and Technology: Compare-and-Contrast Chart

Make a **compare-and-contrast** chart that describes games children can play outdoors. Fill in the chart with details about three games you have played outdoors.

Name of Game	Materials Needed to Play the Game	Room or Weather Needed to Play the Game	Imagination Needed to Play the Game

Dragon, Dragon

John Gardner

Summary A terrible dragon is frightening the people in a kingdom. The king offers a reward to whoever can kill the dragon. A poor cobbler's three sons have different ideas of how to fight the dragon. The father's advice to his sons becomes the key to success.

Reading/Writing Connection

Complete each sentence to describe why you might ask someone for advice.

1. Some people may <u>consult</u> a coach about _____.

2. People should <u>seek</u> advice before _____.

3. <u>Rely</u> on advice only from people _____.

Note-taking Guide

Use this chart to record what happens to each of the cobbler's sons.

	Does he follow his father's advice?	What happens to him?
Eldest son	No, he does not.	
Middle son		
Youngest son		

Dragon, Dragon

1. **Connect:** The elder sons ignore their father's advice about how to kill the dragon. Why do they not believe what he says?

_____

2. **Analyze:** The youngest son kills the dragon. Why is he more successful than his brothers?

_____

3. **Reading Skill:** You **make an inference** when you make a guess based on details in the story. Use the chart below to list details that led you to make an inference about the youngest son. One example is provided. Give one more example.

Details	Inference
He listens to his father's advice.	He trusts his father's wisdom.

4. **Literary Analysis:** Writers use **direct characterization** to tell about a character. Give two examples of direct characterization from the story.

_____

_____

SUPPORT FOR WRITING AND EXTEND YOUR LEARNING

Writing: Help-Wanted Advertisement

Write a **help-wanted ad** for a dragon slayer. Answer the following questions to help you organize information for your ad.

- What would you give a dragon slayer in return for his or her services?

  _____

- What kind of on-the-job training might you provide?

  _____

- What information is usually at the top of an ad?

  _____

- What information needs to be in large or bold print?

  _____

Listening and Speaking: Dramatic Reading

Present a **dramatic reading** of the scene in which the youngest son approaches the cave. Answer the following questions to plan your reading.

- What traits, or qualities, does the youngest son have? How do you know?

  _____

  _____

- What traits, or qualities, does the dragon have? How do you know?

  _____

  _____

- What traits, or qualities, do the elder brothers have? How do you know?

  _____

  _____

Zlateh the Goat • The Old Woman Who Lived With the Wolves

READING SKILL

An **inference** is a logical guess about something that is not directly stated in the text. It is based on information from the text plus your own knowledge. **Prior knowledge** is what you already know. Combine clues from the story with prior knowledge to make an inference. Read the following sentence:

Tina smiled when she saw the snow.

You can infer from this sentence that Tina is happy. Your prior knowledge tells you that people often smile when they are happy. You can infer that snow makes Tina happy.

Use this chart to help you make inferences as you read.

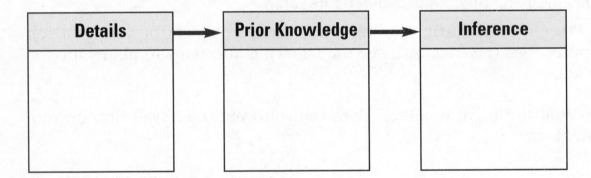

Details	Prior Knowledge	Inference

LITERARY ANALYSIS

A **conflict** is a struggle between two forces. Conflict is an important part of a short story's action. The events help lead to the **resolution**, or the settling of the conflict. A conflict can be:

- **External conflict:** a character struggles against an outside force. This force could be another person or something in nature.

- **Internal conflict:** a character struggles within himself or herself. The struggle could be about making a choice. It could also be about taking an action or fighting a feeling.

A story may have more than one conflict.

Zlateh the Goat

Isaac Bashevis Singer

Summary Reuven needs to sell the family goat, Zlateh. A blizzard hits as Reuven's son Aaron walks the goat to the butcher. The two find shelter in a haystack for three days. Zlateh eats hay. Aaron drinks the goat's milk. Aaron takes the goat back home, and she becomes part of the family.

Reading/Writing Connection

Complete each sentence to describe the dangers of some weather situations.

1. Do not <u>expose</u> _____ in freezing temperatures.

2. Nobody wants to <u>injure</u> _____ when walking in a blizzard.

3. People need to <u>restrict</u> _____ in dangerous weather.

Note-taking Guide

Fill in this chart to help clarify Aaron's character.

Character's Name: Aaron	
What Character Says	**What Character Does**
He asks Zlateh what she thinks about their situation.	He tries to take the goat to the butcher. He finds shelter in a haystack. He keeps the air hole open.
What Character Thinks	**What Others Say About Character**

Zlateh the Goat

1. **Deduce:** Aaron and Zlateh become trapped in a blizzard on their way to town. Why is this dangerous for them?

   _____

   _____

2. **Apply:** Aaron knows after staying in the haystack that he cannot sell Zlateh. What does this story tell you about friendship?

   _____

   _____

3. **Reading Skill:** Aaron's mother and sister cry because Zlateh is going to the butcher. What **inference** can you make about how they feel about the goat?

   _____

   _____

4. **Literary Analysis:** Read each conflict listed in the chart. Tell whether the conflict is **internal** or **external**. Remember that an internal conflict is a struggle inside the person. An external conflict is a struggle with an outside force, such as another person or nature. Use this chart to explain how each conflict was resolved, or settled.

Conflict	What Kind?	Resolution
Reuven needs the money he could get for Zlateh, but he loves Zlateh.		
Aaron and Zlateh need food and shelter but are caught in a blizzard.		

SUPPORT FOR WRITING AND EXTEND YOUR LEARNING

Writing: Persuasive Speech

Write a short **persuasive speech** that Aaron might give to urge his father to keep Zlateh. A persuasive speech tries to convince an audience to believe or do something.

- List three reasons for keeping the goat that Reuven might agree with.

  _____

  _____

  _____

- List three other choices that Aaron could offer in place of selling Zlateh.

  _____

  _____

  _____

- Strengthen your speech by using only the strongest points. Which two or three arguments are most likely to convince Reuven? Circle those reasons.

Listening and Speaking: Monologue

A **monologue** is a speech given by one person. What would Zlateh say about humans' behavior if she could speak? Use this chart to decide which human behaviors to focus on. Fill in details about each type of behavior.

Funniest Behavior	Strangest Behavior	Most Frustrating Behavior

Use these details to write your monologue.

The Old Woman Who Lived With the Wolves

Chief Luther Standing Bear

Summary Marpiyawin's puppy gets lost. She searches for him. A snowstorm forces her to hide in a cave. A pack of wolves helps her stay warm. The wolves lead her to her camp after the snowstorm. Marpiyawin gets a new name because of her friendship with the wolves.

Reading/Writing Connection

Complete each sentence to describe the challenges and feelings that a person lost in the wilderness might face.

1. It would be impossible to <u>survive</u> without _____.

2. Those searching for a lost person would need _____ to <u>locate</u> him or her.

3. Being lost would <u>isolate</u> a person from _____.

Note-taking Guide

Use this chart to record details that show how the characters and animals treat one another in this story.

How Marpiyawin Treats the Wolves	How the Wolves Treat Marpiyawin During the Storm	How Marpiyawin's People Treat the Wolves
She trusts them.		

The Old Woman Who Lived With The Wolves

Chief Luther Standing Bear

A large group of Sioux were on a long walk to a new village. In the group was a young woman named Marpiyawin. She had a pet dog. One night, she couldn't find her dog. She looked everywhere. Then she decided to walk back to the old village. She hoped she would find her dog along the way.

During her long walk, snow started to fall. Cold and tired, Marpiyawin looked for shelter in a dark, warm cave. Soon she fell asleep. She dreamed that she had a wonderful conversation with friendly wolves.

◆ ◆ ◆

. . . They told her that she had lost her way, but that she should trust them and they would not see her suffer from cold or hunger. She replied that she would not worry, and when she awoke it was without fear, even though in the cave with her were the wolves sitting about in a friendly manner.

The blizzard raged outside for many days, still she was contented, for she was neither cold nor hungry. For meat the wolves supplied her with tender rabbits and at night they kept her body warm with their shaggy coats of fur. As the days wore on, she and the wolves became fast friends.

◆ ◆ ◆

Finally, the snow stopped. The wolves offered to take Marpiyawin back to her people. At the end of their walk, they stood on the top of a hill. At the base of the hill, she saw her people. She was sad to say goodbye to the wolves, but she was eager to go home. She thanked them for all of their kindness. She asked whether there was anything she could do to repay them.

◆ ◆ ◆

TAKE NOTES

Activate Prior Knowledge

Share your feelings about a pet that you like. It could be your pet or someone else's.

_____

_____

Literary Analysis

Internal conflict is a struggle that a character faces within himself or herself. **External conflict** happens when a character struggles with an outside force, such as another person or nature.

What is Marpiyawin's conflict in the underlined passage?

_____

_____

Which type of conflict is this?

_____

Reading Skill

Inferences are best guesses. Readers make inferences by looking at the details in a text.

Why is Marpiyawin not afraid of the wolves when she wakes up?

_____

Circle the sentence in the bracketed paragraph that supports your answer.

In English, regular verbs form the past tense by adding –ed. For example, the past tense of the word jump is jumped. Circle the words in the bracketed paragraph that show the past tense of regular verbs.

Read Fluently

Simplify the long underlined sentence by breaking it up into shorter sentences. Circle the subject and underline the predicate in each of your sentences to clarify who is doing what action.

_____

_____

_____

_____

Reading Check

What did the wolves ask Marpiyawin to do for them? Circle the answer.

. . . Marpiyawin thanked all the wolves for their kindness to her and asked what she might do for them. All they asked was that, when the long winter months came and food was <u>scarce</u>, she bring to the top of the hill some nice fat meat for them to eat. This she gladly promised to do and went down the hill toward the camp of her people.

◆ ◆ ◆

Her people were very happy to see her. They had been afraid that she had been captured by enemies. Marpiyawin told them she had been cared for by wolves. She pointed to the hill, where the wolves still sat watching. The people were very surprised. They thought that Marpiyawin must have been in great danger because of the wolves. However, she explained that the wolves had saved her life by feeding her and keeping her warm. She asked them to help her give the wolves food in return. Everyone helped, and Marpiyawin carried the food up the hill to the wolves. She did this again and again, all winter long, and for many winters after that.

◆ ◆ ◆

She never forgot their language and oftentimes in the winter their voices calling to her would be heard throughout the village. Then the people would ask the old woman what the wolves were saying. <u>Their calls would be warnings that a blizzard was coming, or that the enemy was passing close, and to send out a scout or to let the old woman know that they were watching her with care.</u>

And so Marpiyawin came to be known to the tribe as 'The Old Woman Who Lived with the Wolves,' or, in the Sioux language as, 'Win yan wan si k'ma nitu ompi ti.'

Vocabulary Development

scarce (skers) *adj.*   hard to get

The Old Woman Who Lived With the Wolves

1. **Draw Conclusions:** The wolves help Mapiyawin. Would she have lived through the storm without the wolves? Support your answer with details from the story.

_____

_____

2. **Generalize:** The Sioux people have certain ideas about animals and nature. What does Marpiyawin's story show about the way the Sioux view nature?

_____

_____

3. **Reading Skill:** Think of how you felt when you lost something. Make an **inference** about how Marpiyawin feels as she sets out to find her dog.

_____

_____

4. **Literary Analysis:** Use this chart to explain whether each **conflict** is **internal** or **external**. Then, explain how each conflict was resolved.

Conflict	What Kind?	Resolution
Marpiyawin needs food and shelter, but she is lost.		
She is sad to leave the wolves but misses her people.		

SUPPORT FOR WRITING AND EXTEND YOUR LEARNING

Writing: Persuasive Speech

Write a short **persuasive speech** that Marpiyawin might give to urge her people to help the wolves. Answer the following questions to help you write your speech.

• What is the best reason for helping the wolves?

_____

_____

_____

• What argument might people have for not helping the wolves? How could you respond to their arguments?

_____

_____

Research and Technology: Chart

Prepare a **chart** that shows the Sioux people's day-to-day life. Answer the following questions to help you find information for your chart.

• What kinds of books can you use to find information about Sioux settlements?

_____

_____

• What keywords can you use to find information on the Internet about Sioux girls?

_____

_____

Textbooks

ABOUT TEXTBOOKS

A **textbook** gives facts about a subject. A math book or history book that you use in school is a textbook. Textbooks help students learn new information. The information is organized into the following:

- units
- chapters
- sections

Questions and activities in textbooks help students review what they have read.

Textbooks also include **text aids and text features**. Text aids and text features help readers understand and use the information given.

Text Aids	Text Features
• Chapter titles	• Maps, graphs, and charts
• Main headings and subheadings	• Photographs, drawings, and diagrams with captions
• Highlighted vocabulary	

READING SKILL

Text aids and text features organize details in a textbook. They also highlight important information. Here are some tips for using text aids and text features.

Tips for Using Text Aids and Text Features
• Headings and subheadings tell you the main ideas of the chapters.
• Maps, graphs, and charts help you understand the main ideas of the chapters.
• Pictures and diagrams with captions give examples or make clear the main ideas of the chapters.

Farms dot the countryside on the way to the Tatra Mountains in Poland.

The chapter title and the heading highlight the main idea of the chapter. What is the main idea of this chapter?

_____

_____

Read Fluently

Notice the suffixes -ism and -ist in this article. The suffix -ism is used to describe ideas, such as types of governments or religions. The suffix -ist is used to make words that describe people who believe in those ideas and religions. Draw a box around words on this page that have these suffixes.

Reading Skill

Read the underlined sentence. The term **free enterprise** is bold to tell you that this is an important idea. There is a word in the sentence that helps you understand what *free enterprise* means. Circle the helper word.

Culture Note

Folk music and costumed dancing are a large part of Polish culture. It helps people to remember and celebrate their history. Describe a folk music or dance tradition from your native country.

_____

_____

POLAND

Tradition in Poland

Since Poland's communist government fell, the country has moved away from a communist economy in which the government owned and ran all the businesses. Instead, Poland has adopted the **free enterprise** system, or capitalism. In it, people can run their own businesses. But not all of life in Poland has changed. As you travel in the countryside, you see signs of a way of life that existed long before communist rule.

The Polish Countryside For a look at tradition in Poland, you might visit the northeast corner of the country. Here, the Polish border has shifted many times. Again and again, other countries have seized this area. Sometimes, it belonged to Russia. At other times, it was controlled by Lithuania (LITH oo ay nee uh) or Germany. There were even times when other countries took over all of Poland. But no matter what happened, the traditions of Polish life stayed the same. This is true even today.

After World War II, Poland became a communist nation. At public festivals, Poles had to pledge loyalty to communism. When crops did not grow, Poles relied on money from the communist government. When Poles were sick, they went to doctors who were paid by the government. When they were too old to farm, they knew they would receive a government pension.

Now all that has changed. It is up to the farmer to save money for old age. If the crops fail, the farmer must try to borrow money to start again. Learning this new way of life has been hard for some Poles.

The Polish Language Like Roman Catholicism, the language of the Poles has also stood the test of time. Some foreign rulers banned the use of Polish in schools and in the government. The communists did not ban Polish but did force Polish schoolchildren to learn Russian, the main language of the Soviet Union.

Today, the Polish language is alive and well. It ties the people of the nation together and it gives them the strong feeling that being Polish is something different and special. As a Slavic language, it also links the nation to other Slavic nations in Eastern Europe.

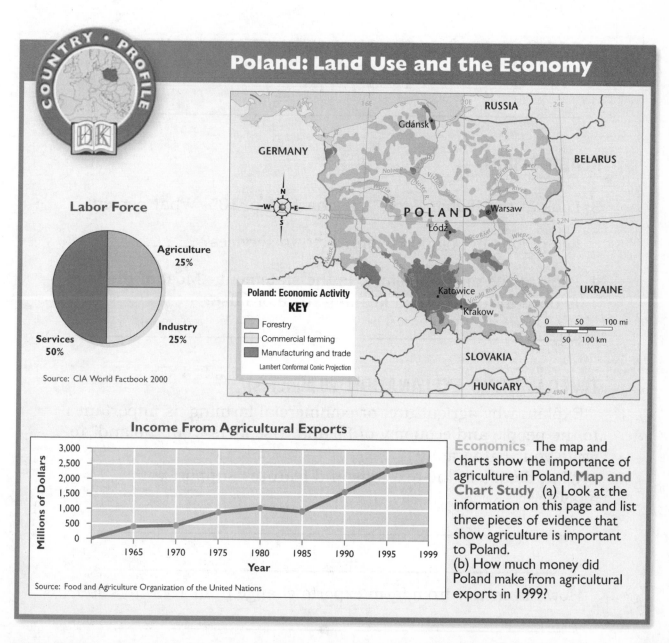

COUNTRY · PROFILE

Poland: Land Use and the Economy

Labor Force

Agriculture 25%

Industry 25%

Services 50%

Source: CIA World Factbook 2000

Poland: Economic Activity
KEY
- Forestry
- Commercial farming
- Manufacturing and trade

Lambert Conformal Conic Projection

RUSSIA

Gdánsk

GERMANY

BELARUS

POLAND Warsaw

Łódź

Katowice

Kraków

UKRAINE

SLOVAKIA

HUNGARY

0   50   100 mi
0   50   100 km

Income From Agricultural Exports

Millions of Dollars

3,000
2,500
2,000
1,500
1,000
500
0

1965 1970 1975 1980 1985 1990 1995 1999

Year

Source: Food and Agriculture Organization of the United Nations

Economics The map and charts show the importance of agriculture in Poland. **Map and Chart Study** (a) Look at the information on this page and list three pieces of evidence that show agriculture is important to Poland.
(b) How much money did Poland make from agricultural exports in 1999?

THINKING ABOUT THE TEXTBOOK

1. Describe one way that life in Poland has changed since the nation has moved from communism to capitalism.

   _____

   _____

2. Is forestry or manufacturing and trade more widespread in Poland?

   _____

   What text feature helped you find the answer?

   _____

READING SKILL

3. Look at the "Labor Force" pie chart on p. 105. What percentage of jobs in Poland is connected to services? _____

4. Look at the map of Poland. Is the statement, "Most of the land is used for commercial farming" true or false?

   _____

TIMED WRITING: EXPLANATION (20 minutes)

Explain why agriculture, or commercial farming, is important to the people and economy of Poland. Use facts from "Poland" to write your paragraph.

What details in the text aids and features support your answer?

_____

_____

How did money from farm exports change from 1960 to 1999?

_____

The All-American Slurp • The Circuit

READING SKILL

A **conclusion** is a thought or an opinion that you form on the basis of what you read. Details help you draw conclusions. **Ask questions** to figure out which details will help you draw conclusions. A good question to ask is *Why is this detail in the story?*

LITERARY ANALYSIS

The **theme** is the main idea of a story. Sometimes an author tells you the theme. Other times, you will need to figure it out.

Fill in this chart with details from the story as you read. The details you record will help you find the theme of the story.

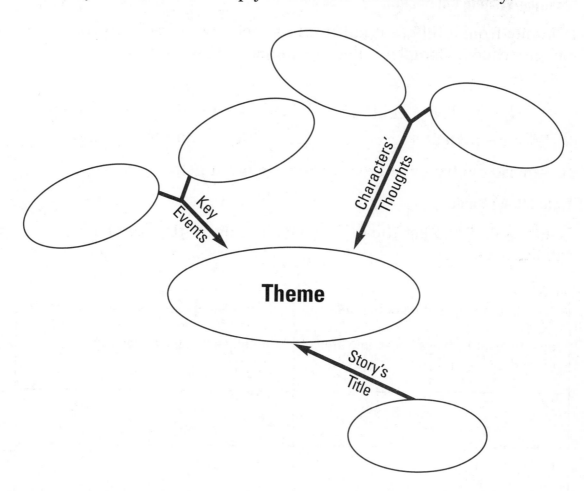

The All-American Slurp

Lensey Namioka

Summary The Lins have moved to the United States from China. People notice the Lins' Chinese habits. The family tries to act more American. One day they invite some American friends for dinner. The Lins find out that they are not as different as they think.

Reading/Writing Connection

A family from a different culture has recently moved into your neighborhood. Complete these sentences to give advice to that family.

1. Many Americans <u>appreciate</u> meeting people from _____.

2. When Americans _____, it is polite to <u>respond</u>.

3. Americans try to settle a <u>conflict</u> before it gets _____.

Note-taking Guide

Use this chart to list the differences in culture that the Lin family faces.

How things are done in China	How things are done in America
Vegetables are always boiled in water before they are served.	Vegetables can be served raw.

The All-American Slurp

1. **Infer:** Each member of the Lin family learns to speak English differently. What does each character's way of learning English tell you about that person?

_____

_____

2. **Compare and Contrast:** Think about how the Lins act at the Gleasons' home. Think about how the Gleasons act at the Lins's home. How are their actions the same?

_____

How are they different?

_____

3. **Reading Skill:** Conclusions are decisions or opinions that you make. You use details in a story to draw these conclusions. Use this chart to **draw conclusions** about the story.

Question	Details That Answer Question	Conclusion
Why do the Gleasons stare as the Lins pull celery strings?		
Why do people in the restaurant stare when the Lins slurp their soup?		

4. **Literary Analysis:** A **theme** is the thought about life that you find in a story. What is the story's theme?

_____

SUPPORT FOR WRITING AND EXTEND YOUR LEARNING

Writing: Description

Write a **description** of a character from "The All-American Slurp." Answer the following questions to gather details for your description.

- What quality do you find most interesting about your character?

  _____

  _____

- How does the character get along with other characters?

  _____

  _____

- What challenges does this character face?

  _____

  _____

Use your answers to write your description.

Listening and Speaking: Interview

Prepare an **interview** with the narrator of the story. To help you to prepare for your interview, write a question and response for these topics.

Topics	Interviewer's Questions	Narrator's Responses
American food	How did you feel when Mrs. Gleason first offered you raw celery?	I was confused. We never eat raw vegetables in China.
American kids		
American dinner parties		
American manners		

Use notes from the chart to conduct your interview.

The Circuit

Francisco Jiménez

Summary Panchito and his family move often to pick crops in California. He is lucky to get to go to school. His teacher, Mr. Lema, offers to teach him to play the trumpet. Panchito rushes home to tell his family. He finds that his life is about to change again.

Reading/Writing Connection

Complete each sentence to describe how changing schools might affect schoolwork and friendships.

1. It would be difficult to <u>adjust</u> to _____.

2. Moving often would <u>affect</u> _____.

3. It takes time to <u>establish</u> _____.

Note-taking Guide

Use this chart to record what Panchito does during certain months.

June and July	August	September and October	November
He picks strawberries.			

Constant change makes life difficult for Panchito. Describe an unexpected change you have faced.

_____

_____

_____

Literary Analysis

The **theme** of a story is its central idea. Read the bracketed passage. It gives clues to the theme of "The Circuit." Underline the words that might suggest the theme. What theme do you think the words suggest?

_____

_____

Reading Check

Why does Panchito's family have to move often? Circle the answer.

The Circuit
Francisco Jiménez

Have you ever moved to a new home? Did it make you feel sad to leave your old home and your old friends behind? Panchito, a young migrant farm worker in Francisco Jiménez's story "The Circuit" has to move often. Migrant worker families can never live too long in one place. They must go wherever the work is. They find jobs picking fruit, harvesting crops, or doing manual labor.

As the story opens, Panchito and his family are getting ready to move again.

◆　◆　◆

It was that time of year again. Ito, the strawberry sharecropper[1] did not smile. It was natural. The peak of the strawberry season was over and the last few days the workers, most of them *braceros,*[2] were not picking as many boxes as they had during the months of June and July.

◆　◆　◆

By the end of August, there are no more strawberries left to pick. Panchito's family will have to look for work somewhere else. Panchito has gotten to like Ito and is sad because he will never see him again. As they drive home, Panchito's older brother Roberto and Papá are silent.

◆　◆　◆

Yes, it was that time of year. When I opened the front door to the shack, I stopped. Everything we owned was neatly packed in cardboard boxes. Suddenly I felt even more the weight of hours, days, weeks, and months of work. I sat down

---

1. **sharecropper** (SHER krahp er) *n.* one who works for a share of the crop.
2. **braceros** (brah SER ohs) *n.* migrant Mexican farm workers who harvest crops.

on a box. The thought of having to move to Fresno[3] and knowing what was in store for me there brought tears to my eyes.

That night I could not sleep. I lay in bed thinking about how much I hated this move.

◆ ◆ ◆

Before dawn, Papá wakes the family. Panchito's little brothers and sisters scream with excitement about the move.

After breakfast, Panchito and Roberto carry boxes out to the car. Papá ties the mattress to the top of the car roof. Mamá brings out her favorite pot filled with beans. Papá places it on the floor behind the front seat. Finally, everything is packed and the whole family is in the car.

◆ ◆ ◆

As we drove away I felt a lump in my throat. I turned around and looked at our little shack for the last time.

◆ ◆ ◆

After driving all day, the family arrives at a labor camp near Fresno. Mama asks if help is needed since Papá cannot speak English.

◆ ◆ ◆

"We don't need no more," said the foreman, scratching his head. "Check with Sullivan down the road. Can't miss him. He lives in a big white house with a fence around it."

◆ ◆ ◆

Mr. Sullivan tells the family he can use them for the whole season. They can live in an old garage with no windows and a roof full of holes.

◆ ◆ ◆

3. **Fresno** (FREZ noh) *n.* city in central California.

TAKE NOTES

Literary Analysis

What do Panchito's tears have to do with the **theme**?

_____

_____

_____

_____

Build English Skills

Read the underlined sentences. A *contraction* is a shortened form of two words. *Don't* is a contraction for *do not*. Circle another contraction in the underlined sentences.

Reading Skill

A **conclusion** is a decision you make based on details in a story. Underline details about the family's new home in the bracketed passage. What can you conclude about the family?

_____

_____

A *prepositional phrase* is a group of words that includes a preposition. A preposition shows the relation, or *position*, of a noun or pronoun to another word. Prepositions include *to, under, from, on,* and *in,* to name a few. Underline the prepositional phrases in the bracketed paragraph.

Culture Note

Panchito is referring to 100 degrees on the Fahrenheit temperature scale. Many countries use a centigrade temperature scale. Which scale do you prefer to use?

_____

_____

Reading Skill

What **conclusion** can you draw in the underlined sentence about why the family works so late?

_____

_____

_____

Reading Check

Underline the text that explains why Papá wants the boys to hide.

That night, by the light of a <u>kerosene</u> lamp, we unpacked and cleaned our new home. Roberto swept away the loose dirt, leaving the hard ground. Papá plugged the holes in the walls with old newspapers and tin can tops. Mamá fed my little brothers and sisters.

◆ ◆ ◆

The family settles in for the night. After breakfast the next morning, Papá, Roberto, and Panchito head for the vineyard to pick grapes.

◆ ◆ ◆

Around nine o'clock the temperature had risen to almost one hundred degrees. I was completely soaked in sweat and my mouth felt as if I had been chewing on a handkerchief.

◆ ◆ ◆

Panchito drinks too much water and gets sick to his stomach. He drops to his knees and stays still on the ground until he starts to feel better. Later, while they are eating lunch, a schoolbus passes by. Papá tells Roberto and Panchito to run and hide in the vineyard. He doesn't want them to get into trouble for not going to school. <u>They work all afternoon until the sun goes down and it gets too dark to see the grapes.</u> The next morning Panchito can hardly move and his body aches all over. This goes on until his muscles get used to the work.

◆ ◆ ◆

It was Monday, the first week of November. The grape season was over and I could now go to school. I woke up early that morning and lay in bed, looking at the stars and <u>savoring</u> the

Vocabulary Development

kerosene (KER uh seen) *n.*   an oil used for burning in heaters and lamps

savoring (SAY ver ing) *v.*   enjoying with appreciation

thought of not going to work and of starting sixth grade for the first time that year.

♦ ♦ ♦

Panchito joins Papá and Roberto at breakfast. He cannot look Roberto in the eye. He knows Roberto has to pick cotton instead of going to school. At eight o'clock Panchito climbs on the schoolbus.

Panchito feels very nervous when he arrives at the school. He has no books like the other children. He goes to the principal's office and is startled when she speaks to him in English. At first, he wants to speak in Spanish, but he finally manages to tell her in English that he wants to enroll in school. Soon, he is taken to the sixth-grade classroom.

♦ ♦ ♦

Mr. Lema, the sixth-grade teacher, greeted me and assigned me a desk. He then introduced me to the class. I was so nervous and scared at that moment when everyone's eyes were on me that I wished I were with Papá and Roberto picking cotton.

♦ ♦ ♦

Mr. Lema gives the class an assignment for their reading hour. He hands Panchito an English book and asks him to read on page 125. When Panchito opens to that page, he cannot begin to read. His mouth is dry and his eyes begin to water. Mr. Lema kindly tells Panchito that he can read later. Panchito gets angry at himself for not reading.

During recess, Panchito tries to read the book in the restroom. He finds many words he does not know. Panchito goes back to the classroom and asks Mr. Lema to help him. "Gladly," says the teacher.

Mr. Lema continues to help Panchito during lunch hour and becomes his best friend.

One day they visit the music room.

TAKE NOTES

Literary Analysis

Do you think that Panchito has ever enrolled at a new school before? Explain.

_____

_____

_____

How does this relate to the **theme**?

_____

_____

_____

_____

Reading Skill

Panchito is nervous when Mr. Lema introduces him to the class. What **conclusion** do you draw from Panchito's feelings?

_____

_____

_____

_____

Reading Check

What does Panchito do to learn English? Circle the text that tells what he does.

Stop to Reflect

Do you think that Mr. Lema is a good teacher? Explain.

_____

_____

_____

_____

Vocabulary and Pronunciation

The word *circuit* is pronounced (SER kit). Circuit can mean (a) the act of going around something, (b) a regular journey from place to place, ending up in the first place, (c) a complete path through which electrical current can flow. Circle the meaning that is used in the title.

Reading Check

What does the narrator find when he gets home from school? Underline the text that tells you.

Mr. Lema asks Panchito if he likes music and begins to play a trumpet. The sound of the trumpet gives Panchito *goose bumps.* Mr. Lema asks him if he would like to learn to play it.

♦ ♦ ♦

He must have read my face because before I could answer, he added: "I'll teach you how to play it during our lunch hours."

That day I could hardly wait to get home to tell Papá and Mamá the great news. As I got off the bus, my little brothers and sisters ran up to meet me. They were yelling and screaming. I thought they were happy to see me, but when I opened the door to our shack, I saw that everything we owned was neatly packed in cardboard boxes.

The Circuit

1. **Respond:** What do you admire about Panchito? Why?

   _____

   _____

2. **Infer:** It is difficult for Panchito to make friends in new places. Why do you think Panchito calls Mr. Lema his "best friend at school"?

   _____

   _____

   _____

3. **Reading Skill:** A **conclusion** is a decision you make based on the details in a story. Complete this chart to **draw conclusions** about what happens in the story.

Question	Details That Answer Question	Conclusion
Why does Panchito work so much?		
Why are the family's belongings packed in boxes?		

4. **Literary Analysis:** How does the title of this story connect to its **theme**?

   _____

   _____

SUPPORT FOR WRITING AND EXTEND YOUR LEARNING

Writing: Character Description

Write a **description** of a character from "The Circuit." Answer the following questions to gather details for your description.

- What quality do you find most interesting about your character?

_____

_____

- How does this character get along with other characters?

_____

_____

- What challenges does this character face?

_____

_____

Use your answers to write your description.

Research and Technology: Report

Research the lives of migrant workers to prepare a brief **report**. Answer the following questions as you complete your research:

- From what country do many of the migrant workers in the United States come?

_____

- During what times of year do they come?

_____

- What ages are the workers?

_____

Use your answers to add details to your report.

© Pearson Education, Inc., publishing as Pearson Prentice Hall.

The King of Mazy May • Aaron's Gift

READING SKILL

Drawing conclusions means making a decision or opinion about what happens in a story. Readers draw conclusions by using details in the story. They may also use **prior knowledge**, or things they already know from experience to draw conclusions.

Use this chart to help you draw conclusions as you read.

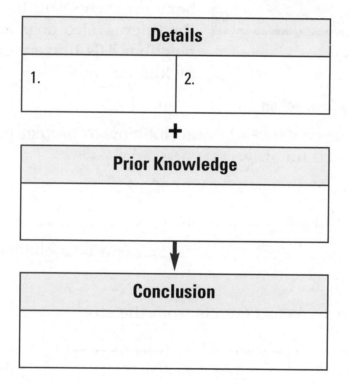

Details	
1.	2.

+

Prior Knowledge

↓

Conclusion

LITERARY ANALYSIS

The **setting** of a story is where and when the story takes place.

Time may be the past, present, or future. It may also be the season of the year or the hour of the day.

The place may be a country or city. It may also be a certain street, house, or public place. Pay attention to the way that setting affects characters and events in the story as you read.

The King of Mazy May

Jack London

Summary Walt and his father live in the far North, where people search for gold. Walt is left alone on their land one day. He watches as thieves prepare to steal a neighbor's property. Walt takes some of the thieves' sled dogs to warn the neighbor. His bravery earns him his nickname.

Reading/Writing Connection

Complete these sentences to describe how to protect people who are being treated unfairly.

1. It is right to <u>challenge</u> someone if _____.

2. People should <u>plead</u> to protect _____.

3. Doing _____ can be a <u>challenge</u>.

Note-taking Guide

Use this chart to record details from the story.

Why does Loren Hall go to Dawson?	Why does Walt go to Dawson?	Why do the men follow Walt?
Loren Hall goes to Dawson to register his claim.		

The King of Mazy May

Jack London

Have you ever wondered what it would be like to live in the wilderness? Walt Masters, a fourteen-year-old boy in Jack London's story "The King of Mazy May," has lived his whole life in the lonely Yukon wilderness. He and his father have been prospecting for gold and have filed a claim. While Walt's father and their neighbor Loren Hall are away, Walt comes across men planning to steal Hall's claim.

The story opens with a description of Walt and details about his life:

Walt Masters is not a very large boy, but in some ways he is like a man. There are many things he has never seen, because he has lived in the wilderness all his life. He has never seen a train or an elevator, nor has he ever seen a farm, a plow, a cow, or even a chicken. He has never gone to a picnic or party, nor talked to a girl. But he has seen the sun at midnight and played beneath the northern lights.

Walt is the only young white boy in thousands of square miles of frozen wilderness. He can trade with the Indians for their precious furs. He can bake bread and shoot a moose. He can also drive his team of wild wolf dogs fifty miles a day on the snow-packed trail.

◆ ◆ ◆

Walt was born a thousand miles or so down the Yukon,[1] in a trading post below the Ramparts. After his mother died, his father and he came up on the river, step by step, from camp to camp, till now they are settled down on the Mazy May

---

1. **Yukon** (YOO kahn) river flowing through the Yukon Territory of northwest Canada.

TAKE NOTES

Activate Prior Knowledge

What do you already know about what it is like to live in a cold climate?

_____

_____

_____

Vocabulary and Pronunciation

The word *claim* can be used as a noun or a verb. How is it being used here?

_____

What does it mean? Circle the correct answer.
(a) a fact
(b) ownership of something
(c) a rough place
(d) a gold nugget

Literary Analysis

The **setting** of a story is the time and place of the action. Describe the setting of this story.

_____

_____

Reading Check

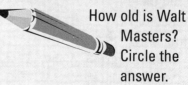

How old is Walt Masters? Circle the answer.

The Klondike Gold Rush began in 1896 after George Carmack discovered gold in the Klondike region of northwestern Canada. Thousands of other people followed Carmack. Most people found hard times but no gold.

Stop to Reflect

What do you think are some of the hardships that the settlers had to endure?

_____

_____

_____

Reading Skill

Walt has been given many responsibilities while his father is away. **Draw a conclusion** about Walt based on this detail. What does his ability to look after his father's claim tell you about Walt's character?

_____

_____

_____

Reading Check

What began to happen after the hard work of the settlers started to pay off? Underline the answer.

Creek in the Klondike country. Last year they and several others had spent much <u>toil</u> and time on the Mazy May, and <u>endured</u> great hardships; the creek, in turn, was just beginning to show up its richness and to reward them for their heavy labor. But with the news of their discoveries, strange men began to come and go through the short days and long nights, and many unjust things they did to the men who had worked so long upon the creek.

◆ ◆ ◆

One of the prospectors goes hunting. He returns to the creek to find his claim jumped. Others lose their claims by taking too long to reach Dawson to record them.

◆ ◆ ◆

But Walt Masters's father had recorded his claim from the start, so Walt had nothing to fear now that his father had gone on a short trip up the White River prospecting for quartz. Walt was well able to stay by himself in the cabin, cook his three meals a day, and look after things. Not only did he look after his father's claim, but he had agreed to keep an eye on the adjoining one of Loren Hall, who had started for Dawson to record it.

◆ ◆ ◆

Loren Hall is an old man. He travels very slowly because he has no dogs and has to walk. At Rosebud Creek Loren falls through the ice and his feet are frozen. He is not able to travel for a couple of weeks. Then Walt gets word that Loren is better and is getting ready to travel again.

◆ ◆ ◆

Vocabulary Development

toil (toyl) *n.*   hard work
endured (in DOORD) *v.*   suffered through

Walt was worried, however; the claim was liable to be jumped at any moment because of this delay, and a fresh stampede had started in on the Mazy May. He did not like the looks of the newcomers, and one day, when five of them came by with crack dog teams and the lightest of camping outfits, he could see that they were prepared to make speed, and resolved to keep an eye on them. So he locked up the cabin and followed them, being at the same time careful to remain hidden.

◆ ◆ ◆

Walt sees the men change many stakes, destroy old ones, and set up new ones. He creeps up to their camp, close enough to hear what they are saying. The leader, a big man with a black beard, tells the others that they should head back to Dawson tonight.

◆ ◆ ◆

"That's it," said the leader. "If we can get to Dawson and record, we're rich men; and there's no telling who's been sneaking along in our tracks, watching us, and perhaps now off to give the alarm. The thing for us to do is to rest the dogs a bit, and then hit the trail as hard as we can. What do you say?"

◆ ◆ ◆

The other men agree. Before they get ready to leave, the leader takes three of his men to check on one last claim. Walt follows them to Loren Hall's claim. The men scoop up a couple of buckets of dirt. They put the dirt in a pan and wash it in the creek.

◆ ◆ ◆

Vocabulary Development

liable (LY uh buhl) *adj.*   likely to do something

stampede (stam PEED) *n.*   a sudden mass movement of people

resolved (ri ZAHLVD) *v.*   decided

The King of Mazy May **113**

TAKE NOTES

Reading Skill

Read the bracketed paragraph. **Draw a conclusion** about Walt's feelings. What does Walt's behavior tell you about his attitude toward the men?

_____

_____

_____

Read Fluently

Break long sentences down into smaller sentences to understand them. Simplify the underlined sentence by breaking it up into shorter sentences. Mark the break with a line.

Literary Analysis

Characters' actions depend on the **setting**. How does the time of the story affect the characters' travel choices?

_____

_____

Vocabulary and Pronunciation

What do you think the underlined phrase means? Circle the correct answer.
  (a) beat dirt with a stick
  (b) punch the road
  (c) go as fast as we can
  (d) spend the night here

Walt feels that he must do something to protect Loren Hall's claim. What does this tell you about Walt's character? Answer this question by **drawing** your own **conclusions**.

_____

_____

_____

In order to stop the thieves, Walt decides to steal their dogs. Do you agree with his decision? Explain.

_____

_____

_____

_____

Draw a **conclusion** about why it would be impossible to travel seventy miles to Dawson without dogs.

_____

_____

_____

What made Walt decide to steal the dogs and travel to Dawson? Underline the answer.

When this was finished, they stared at the broad streak of black sand and yellow gold grains on the bottom of the pan, and one of them called excitedly for the man who had remained in camp to come. Loren Hall had struck it rich and his claim was not yet recorded. It was plain that they were going to jump it.

Walt lay in the snow, thinking rapidly. He was only a boy, but in the face of the threatened injustice to old lame Loren Hall he felt that he must do something. He waited and watched, with his mind made up, till he saw the men begin to square up new stakes.

♦ ♦ ♦

Walt crawls away till he is out of hearing. Then he breaks into a run for the camp of the claim jumpers. Walt's father has taken their own dogs with him prospecting. Walt knows that he cannot go the seventy miles to Dawson without the aid of dogs. So when he reaches the camp, he picks out the ten best dogs and harnesses them to one of the sleds. Just then the claim jumpers come into sight. As they cry out to Walt, he grabs one of their fur sleeping robes. He leaps upon the sled and takes off.

♦ ♦ ♦

"Mush! Hi! Mush on!" he cried to the animals, snapping the keen-lashed whip among them.

♦ ♦ ♦

The dogs race along the frozen creek bed, pulling Walt on the sled. He can hear the cries of the claim jumpers as they run along the high creek bank to cut him off. Walt's heart is beating wildly. Suddenly, one of the men leaps at the sled. He grabs onto one end of the sled and is dragged along behind it. Walt cracks him across the knuckles with his whip until he has to let go.

For the next eight miles the Mazy May follows a crooked course until it meets the Yukon. Two of the men take a shortcut across a narrow neck of land. At the next bend in the creek, they have almost caught up to Walt.

◆   ◆   ◆

"Halt!" they cried after him. "Stop, or we'll shoot!" But Walt only yelled harder at the dogs, and dashed around the bend with a couple of revolver bullets singing after him. At the next bend they had drawn up closer still, and the bullets struck uncomfortably near him but at this point the Mazy May straightened out and ran for half a mile as the crow flies. Here the dogs stretched out in their long wolf swing, and the stampeders, quickly winded, slowed down and waited for their own sled to come up.

◆   ◆   ◆

Walt knows that they have not given up the chase and will soon be after him again. It is twilight by the time Walt comes upon the mighty frozen Yukon. The sled flies along the glassy ice of the main river trail. At times it becomes necessary to guide the dogs by his voice. Walt now learns that he has made a mistake in his choice of lead dog. This dog has never learned the meaning of "gee" and "haw." Several times he capsizes the sled.

With the air temperature at forty below, Walt knows he will freeze to death if he remains constantly upon the sled. Every now and then he jumps off the sled and runs behind it until he warms up. When Walt looks back, he can now see the sled of the claim jumpers.

◆   ◆   ◆

Night fell, and in the blackness of the first hour or so Walt toiled desperately with his dogs. On account of the lead dog, they were continually floundering off the beaten track into the soft snow, and the sled was as often riding on its side or top as it was in the proper way.

◆   ◆   ◆

When the moon rises, Walt can see that his enemies have come within four hundred yards of him. They begin firing at him with a

Literary Analysis

The **setting** can affect a character's actions in a story. What details about the Mazy May make it hard for Walt to travel to Dawson?

_____

_____

Build English Skills

An idiom is an expression whose meaning does not follow the actual meaning of its words. The expression "Jim *breezed* through the test" is an idiom meaning *Jim finished the test quickly and easily.* Underline an idiom in the first bracketed passage. Use the idiom in a sentence of your own.

_____

_____

_____

Literary Analysis

The **setting** has changed at this point in the story. Read the second bracketed paragraph. Circle the detail that shows a change in time. Put a star next to the detail that shows a change in place.

Draw conclusions about why Walt falls asleep when the sled pulls into Dawson.

_____

_____

_____

_____

Explain the title of this story, "The King of Mazy May."

_____

_____

_____

What happens when Walt throws the claim jumpers' lead dog? Circle the answer.

rifle. Suddenly a bullet strikes Walt's bad lead dog. Walt stops to drag the dying animal to the side and straighten out the team.

As Walt leaps back upon the sled, the claim jumpers come up alongside him. Walt strikes at their faces with his whip. Then he reaches out, catches their lead dog by the forelegs, and throws him. This capsizes the sled, snarls the team, and tangles up Walt's enemies.

◆ ◆ ◆

Away Walt flew, the runners of his sled fairly screaming as they bounded over the frozen surface. And what had seemed an accident proved to be a blessing in disguise. The proper lead dog was now to the fore, and he stretched low and whined with joy as he jerked his comrades along.

◆ ◆ ◆

Walt leaves the claim jumpers far behind. At daylight he reaches Swede Creek and runs into the camp of old Loren Hall. Loren quickly joins Walt on the sled. There is no sign of the claim jumpers. Just as they pull up at the gold commissioner's office in Dawson, Walt falls asleep.

◆ ◆ ◆

And because of what Walt Masters did on this night, the men of the Yukon have become proud of him, and speak of him now as the King of Mazy May.

The King of Mazy May

1. **Compare and Contrast:** Think about the responsibilities that most kids have. How is Walt's life different from those of other children his age?

   _____

   _____

2. **Apply:** Would you have been tempted to travel to the Klondike in search of gold? Explain.

   _____

   _____

3. **Reading Skill:** People call Walt the "King of Mazy May." Use your **prior knowledge** to **draw a conclusion** about how Walt feels about his new name.

   _____

4. **Literary Analysis:** Use this chart to list ways in which details of the **setting** affect events in the story.

	Details of Setting	Story Events
Time		
Place		

SUPPORT FOR WRITING AND EXTEND YOUR LEARNING

Writing: Personal Narrative

Write a short **personal narrative** about a time when you worked hard to meet a goal. Answer these questions to help you get started:

• What was the goal?

_____

• What was the first thing that happened?

_____

• What happened before you met your goal?

_____

_____

• What happened when you finally reached your goal?

_____

_____

Use your answers to write your narrative in the correct order.

Research and Technology: Presentation

Prepare a **presentation** on gold mining. Be sure to use reliable sources, such as encyclopedias or Web sites that are managed by schools. Use this chart to organize your research.

Source	Information Found	Reliable? Yes or No

Use your chart to prepare your presentation.

Aaron's Gift

Myron Levoy

Summary Ten-year-old Aaron fixes a hurt pigeon's wing. Aaron plans to give the bird to his grandmother. A gang of neighborhood boys tries to burn the pigeon. Aaron is beaten up while trying to save the bird. The bird flies away. Aaron is surprised that he has still given a gift to his grandmother.

Reading/Writing Connection

Complete these sentences to describe how to find new ways to solve problems.

1. To think of new ideas, <u>rely</u> on _____.

2. Finding a new approach can help people <u>accomplish</u> _____.

3. Try to <u>adjust</u> a viewpoint to _____.

Note-taking Guide

Use this chart to record the most important events of the story.

Where does Aaron find the pigeon?	
How does Aaron help it?	
Who invites Aaron to join her club?	
What happens when the boys try to burn the pigeon?	
Why is his grandmother grateful?	

Aaron's Gift

1. **Compare and Contrast:** How are Carl and the boys like the Cossacks?

_____

2. **Apply:** Aaron's grandmother thinks the bird's freedom is a gift. Think of some other "gifts" that are not things a person could buy, find, or make. Explain why these things are important.

_____

_____

3. **Reading Skill:** Use your **prior knowledge** to explain why Aaron's mother will not let him play with Carl and the others.

_____

5. **Literary Analysis:** Complete the chart to tell how details of the **setting** affect events in the story.

	Details of Setting	Story Events
Time		
Place		

SUPPORT FOR WRITING AND EXTEND YOUR LEARNING

Writing: Personal Narrative

Write a short **personal narrative** about a time when you worked hard to meet a goal. Answer these questions to help you get started:

• What was the goal?

_____

• What happened before you met your goal?

_____

_____

• What happened when you finally reached your goal?

_____

_____

Listening and Speaking: Speech

As Aaron, you will give a **speech** honoring his grandmother on her birthday. Focus on these questions:

• What are the highlights of Aaron's grandmother's life?

_____

_____

• What does Aaron admire about his grandmother?

_____

_____

• Why is this birthday special?

_____

_____

Comparison-and-Contrast Articles

ABOUT COMPARISON-AND-CONTRAST ARTICLES

A **comparison-and-contrast article** is descriptive writing. This type of writing looks at what is alike and what is different about two or more subjects. There are two common ways of organizing these articles.

- **Block organization:** First, the writer gives all of the details of one subject. Then, the writer gives all of the details of the other subject.

- **Point-by-point organization:** First, the writer gives one detail about both subjects. Then, the writer gives another detail about both subjects.

READING SKILL

The best way to understand a comparison-and-contrast article is by **identifying and analyzing the organization**.

Identifying: First, identify what kind of organization the writer uses. Then, use the organization to find the main points. This method will help you understand how the subjects are alike and different.

Analyzing: Study the information by breaking it into parts and groups. Ask yourself questions like the ones in the chart to evaluate the comparisons.

Questions for evaluating comparison-and-contrast organization
Are the same categories covered for each half of the comparison?
Is an approximately equal number of details supplied for each category?
Does the writer support compare-and-contrast statements with examples and facts?

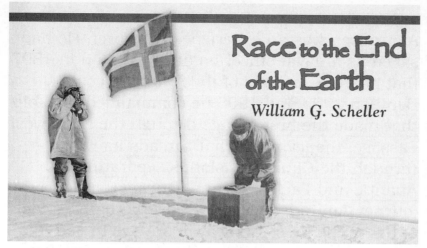

Race to the End of the Earth

William G. Scheller

Amundsen's team proving South Pole location

Two explorers competed against each other and a brutal environment to reach the South Pole.

The drifts were so deep and the snow was falling so heavily that the team of five Norwegian explorers could hardly see their sled dogs a few feet ahead of them. Behind rose a monstrous mountain barrier. The men had been the first to cross it. But now they and their dogs were stumbling toward a stark and desolate plateau continually blasted by blizzards. The landscape was broken only by the towering peaks of mountains that lay buried beneath a mile of ancient ice. Led by Roald Amundsen, the men were still 300 miles from their goal: the South Pole.

On that same day, a party of 14 British explorers was also struggling across a similarly terrifying landscape toward the same destination. But they were almost twice as far from success. Their commander was Capt. Robert Falcon Scott, a naval officer. Amundsen was Scott's rival.

Preparation Both expedition leaders had long been preparing for their race to the South Pole. Amundsen came from a family of hardy sailors, and he had decided at the age of 15 to become a polar explorer. He conditioned himself by taking long ski trips across the Norwegian countryside and by sleeping with his windows open in winter.

Reading Comparison-and-Contrast Articles

The boldface word on this page is a heading. The headings tell you what the writer will compare in the next section of the article. What is the first thing the writer is going to compare?

_____

_____

Reading Skill

Contrast the progress of the two expeditions. Which expedition has been more successful so far?

_____

_____

Stop to Reflect

What do you think are the dangers involved in traveling to the South Pole?

_____

_____

_____

Reading Check

How many explorers were on Scott's team? Circle the answers in the text.

Reading Comparison-and-Contrast Articles

The first part of this article discusses how Scott and Amundsen prepared for their expeditions. **Identify** the method of organization the writer uses to present similarities and differences.

_____

_____

Reading Fluently

The comma in the underlined sentence is used to set off words that describe the Northwest Passage. Circle two other sentences on this page that also use a comma to set off a description.

Reading Skill

In the bracketed paragraph, the writer begins to **analyze** the differences that affected the outcome of the race. What is the most important word in the first sentence? Explain how this word lets readers know what is to come in the article.

_____

_____

_____

By the time of his South Pole attempt, Amundsen was an experienced explorer. He had sailed as a naval officer on an expedition in 1897 that charted sections of the Antarctic coast. Between 1903 and 1906 he commanded the ship that made the first voyage through the Northwest Passage, the icy route that threads its way through the Canadian islands separating the Atlantic and Pacific Oceans. During that long journey Amundsen learned how the native people of the Arctic dress and eat to survive in extreme cold. He also learned that the dogsled was the most efficient method of polar transportation. These lessons would serve him well at Earth's frozen southern end.

Robert Scott was an officer in the British Navy. He had decided that leading a daring expedition of discovery would be an immediate route to higher rank. He heard that Great Britain's Royal Geographical Society was organizing such an exploration, and he volunteered in 1899 to be its commander. Now he was in command again.

The two expedition leaders had different styles. Scott followed a British tradition of brave sacrifice. He felt that he and his men should be able to reach the South Pole with as little help as possible from sled dogs and special equipment. He did bring dogs to Antarctica, as well as 19 ponies and three gasoline-powered sledges, or sturdy sleds. But his plan was for his team to "man-haul," or carry, all of their own supplies along the final portion of the route.

Scott's
ill-fated team

Roald Amundsen had spent much time in the far north, and he was a practical man. He'd seen how useful dogs were to Arctic inhabitants. He would be traveling in one of the most dangerous places on Earth, and he knew that sled dogs would be able to get his party all the way to the South Pole and make a safe return. Amundsen also placed great faith in skis, which he and his Norwegian team members had used since childhood. The British explorers had rarely used skis before this expedition and did not understand their great value.

The two leaders even had different ideas about diet. Scott's men would rely on canned meat. But Amundsen's plan made more sense. He and his men would eat plenty of fresh seal meat. Amundsen may not have fully understood the importance of vitamins, but fresh meat is a better source of vitamin C, which prevents scurvy, a painful and sometimes deadly disease.

The Race Is On! After making long sea voyages from Europe, Scott and Amundsen set up base camps in January on opposite edges of the Ross Ice Shelf. Each team spent the dark winter months making preparations to push on to the Pole when spring would arrive in Antarctica. Amundsen left base camp on October 20, 1911, with a party of four. Scott, accompanied by nine men, set off from his camp 11 days later. Four others had already gone ahead on the motorized sledges.

<u>Scott's final diary entry</u> Things went wrong for Scott from the beginning. The sledges broke down and had to be abandoned. Scott and his men soon met up with the drivers, who were traveling on foot. Blizzards then struck and lasted several weeks into December. Scott's ponies were proving to be a poor choice for Antarctic travel as well. Their hooves sank deep into the snow, and their perspiration froze on their bodies, forming sheets of ice. (Dogs do not perspire; they pant.) On December 9, the men

Reading Skill

The bracketed paragraph ends with a comparison of the teams' attitudes toward skis.

Identify the type of organization the writer uses here.

_____

How do the teams differ in their opinions about using skis?

_____

_____

_____

Culture Note

Amundsen's team used skis to reach the South Pole. Skiing is a very popular sport in America. Some of the most popular places to ski are in Colorado.

Reading Comparison-and-Contrast Articles

What clue does the **article's** underlined heading give you about the outcome of Scott's expedition?

_____

_____

_____

_____

Reading Check

When did Amundsen leave base camp? Underline the answer in the text.

Read the bracketed paragraphs. The writer describes the problems that the teams had in trying to reach the South Pole. Underline the details that describe Scott's difficulties. Then, circle the details about Amundsen's difficulties. Analyze the details. Which problems could have been avoided? Explain.

_____

_____

_____

What lesson can be learned from this article?

_____

_____

_____

Why is it important to look at a writer's comparison-and-contrast organization?

_____

_____

_____

shot the last of the surviving weak and frozen ponies. Two days later Scott sent his remaining dogs back to base camp along with several members of the expedition. Over the next month, most of the men returned to the camp. Scott's plan from here on was for the five men remaining to man-haul supplies the rest of the way to the Pole and back.

For Scott and his men, the journey was long and brutal. To cover only ten miles each day, the team toiled like dogs—like the dogs they no longer had. Food and fuel were in short supply, so the men lacked the energy they needed for such a crushing task.

Roald Amundsen's careful planning and Arctic experience were paying off. Even so, there's no such thing as easy travel by land in Antarctica. To the men who had just crossed those terrible mountains, the Polar Plateau might have looked easy. But Amundsen's team still had to cross a long stretch they later named the "Devil's Ballroom." It was a thin crust of ice that concealed crevasses, or deep gaps, that could swallow men, sleds, and dogs. Stumbling into one crevasse, a team of dogs dangled by their harnesses until the men could pull them up to safety.

Reaching the Goal On skis, with the "ballroom" behind them and well-fed dogs pulling their supply sleds, Amundsen and his men swept across the ice. The going was smooth for them, and the weather was fine. The Norwegian's only worry was that they'd find Scott had gotten to the Pole first. On the afternoon of December 14, 1911, it was plain that no one was ahead of them. At three o'clock, Amundsen skied in front of the team's sleds, then stopped to look at his navigation instruments. There was no point further south. He was at the South Pole!

THINKING ABOUT THE COMPARISON-AND-CONTRAST ARTICLE

1. Contrast the strategies used by each team.

   Scott: _____

   Amundsen: _____

2. Evaluate the organization of "Race to the End of the Earth." Does the writer balance the details? Describe an example.

   _____

   _____

READING SKILL

3. Describe a major difference between Scott and Amundsen.

   _____

4. Describe a similarity in the backgrounds of the two men.

   _____

TIMED WRITING: ANALYSIS (20 minutes)

Analyze the reasons why Amundsen reached the South Pole before Scott. Use this chart to organize details from the article.

	Amundsen	Scott
Preparation		
Dogs and special equipment		
Diet		

ADDING THE SUFFIXES -*ED* AND -*ING*

Adding a suffix to a word can change its spelling. Knowing the rules can help you spell words with suffixes correctly.

RULES FOR ADDING THE SUFFIXES -*ED* AND -*ING*

- The base word sometimes does not change.
  (*answer* + *ed* = *answered*)
- If the base word ends in *e*, drop the *e*.
  (*decide* + *ed* = *decided*; *decide* + *ing* + *deciding*)
- If a two-syllable word ends with a stressed syllable, often double the final consonant. (*omit* + *ed* = *omitted*; *omit* + *ing* = *omitting*)
- If the base word ends in *y*, change the *y* to *i* before adding -*ed*. (*satisfy* + *ed* = *satisfied*)
- If the base word ends in *y*, keep the *y* before adding -*ing*. (*satisfy* + *ing* = *satisfying*)

Word List
answered
deciding
omitted
satisfied
satisfying
occurring
interfered
exercising
delaying
occurred

Practice Read the following paragraph. Circle any word that is misspelled. Then, write the misspelled word correctly on the lines below.

Before decideing to go to the party, Jen wanted to figure out what to wear. She rememberred that many of her friends would be wearing jeans and tee-shirts. It occured to her that she could wear that, too. After trying on three pairs of jeans and seven tee-shirts, Jen was finally satisfyed with her outfit.

_____

_____

_____

_____

Zlata's Diary

Nonfiction writing is about real people, places, ideas, and experiences. Sometimes the author tells stories from his or her life.

The **organization** of nonfiction writing is important. Essays and articles need to be clear and easy to follow. This chart lists different types of organization.

Organization	Definition	Example
Chronological	• presents details in time order, from first to last or even from last to first	a vacation journal
Cause-and-effect	• shows relationships among events	essay about reasons why a neighborhood pool closed and the effect the pool's closing has on kids in the neighborhood
Comparison-and-contrast	• shows ways in which two or more subjects are similar and different	essay that compares how two schools are the same and different

How an author thinks about a subject is important. The following list tells about the importance of the author in nonfiction writing.

- **Author's influence:** Everyone has a different background, culture, and personal beliefs. Authors are shaped by these experiences.

- **Author's style:** Every author has a different writing style. An author's style can be formal, friendly, or even funny.

- **Mood:** The mood is the overall feeling created by an essay or article. The mood of a piece of writing can depend on an author's influence and style.

- **Author's purpose:** Every author has a purpose, or reason, for writing. The purpose helps the writer decide which details to include. Some purposes are to entertain, to inform, or to persuade.

The following are some types of nonfiction writing:

Letters, journals, and diaries: a person's thoughts and memories

Biographies and autobiographies: stories about a person's life

- **Biography:** story about a person's life that is written by another person

- **Autobiography:** story a person writes about his or her own life

Media accounts: newspaper and magazine articles, television or radio reports

Essays and articles: short works that focus on a certain subject

- **Historical writing:** gives facts and explains historic events

- **Persuasive writing:** persuades readers to take an action or change their minds

- **Descriptive writing:** appeals to the five senses (sight, hearing, taste, touch, smell)

- **Expository writing:** presents facts, discusses ideas, or explains a process

- **Narrative writing:** tells the story of real-life experiences

- **Visual writing:** uses words and pictures or graphs to share information

- **Reflective writing:** tells why an event is important to the author

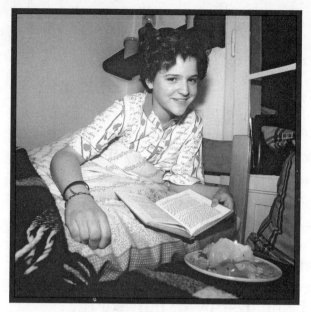

Zlata's Diary

Zlata Filipović

Summary Zlata Filipović is a young girl in fifth grade in Sarajevo. She begins to keep a diary as a war is beginning in her country. Her diary becomes a journal of the war. She writes about the difficulties that her family, her friends, and her city face.

Note-taking Guide

Fill in this chart with details about Zlata.

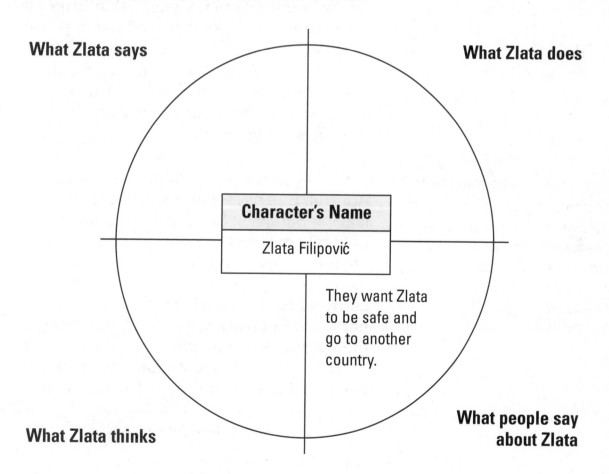

What Zlata says

What Zlata does

Character's Name

Zlata Filipović

They want Zlata to be safe and go to another country.

What Zlata thinks

What people say about Zlata

Describe why a person may keep a diary or journal.

_____

_____

_____

_____

Nonfiction

Chronological organization shows details and information in time order. What clues tell you that this diary is written this way?

_____

_____

_____

_____

Nonfiction

An **author's purpose** is his or her reason for writing. Underline the sentence that describes what Zlata sees on TV. What is her purpose for including these details?

_____

_____

_____

Zlata's Diary
Zlata Filipović

Zlata decides to name her diary Mimmy.[1] She begins her first letter to Mimmy on March 30, 1992. She tells Mimmy that war has struck her country, and rumors say that her city of Sarajevo may be bombed on April 4. She is very frightened.

Her next letter to Mimmy is dated April 12.

◆ ◆ ◆

The new sections of town—Dobrinja, Mojmilo, Vojnicko polje—are being badly <u>shelled</u>. Everything is being destroyed, burned, the people are in shelters. Here in the middle of town, where we live, it's different. It's quiet. People go out. It was a nice warm spring day today. We went out too. Vaso Miskin Street was full of people, children. It looked like a peace march. People came out to be together, they don't want war. They want to live and enjoy themselves the way they used to. That's only natural, isn't it? Who likes or wants war, when it's the worst thing in the world?

◆ ◆ ◆

Zlata's next letter to Mimmy is dated April 14. She says that many people are leaving Sarajevo. She has seen sad pictures of family members saying goodbye to each other on television news programs. She wonders why such innocent people have to suffer so badly. Zlata knows that her own parents don't know what to do—whether they should leave or stay.

In her letter of May 2, Zlata says that this day was the worst day ever. The shooting

---

Vocabulary Development

shelled (sheld) *v.* bombed

---

1. **Mimmy** (MEE mee)

started at noon. Zlata and her mother went into the hall of their apartment to get away from the windows. Her father was downstairs in his office. They grabbed Zlata's canary Cicko and ran downstairs to meet him. Then they all went to hide in the dark cellar. They could hear the sounds of guns, bombs, and airplanes.

They return to their apartment that night. Their neighborhood has been badly damaged. Zlata is worried about her grandparents. They live in another neighborhood that has had even worse damage.

She writes her next letter to Mimmy on May 5. She reports that the shooting has died down a little. She thinks that the warring sides are trying to come to an agreement.

◆ ◆ ◆

. . . Oh, if only they would, so we could live and breathe as human beings again. The things that have happened here these past few days are terrible. I want it to stop forever. PEACE! PEACE!

◆ ◆ ◆

She tells Mimmy that she and her parents no longer sleep in their bedrooms. It is too dangerous because of the shooting. So now they sleep away from the windows on mattresses on the floor of the sitting room. Her canary now lives in the kitchen. They will move back to the cellar if the shooting and bombing gets really bad again.

Her next letter is dated May 7. She reports that a bomb landed in a park where she used to play. Many people were hurt. Her friend Nina was killed.

◆ ◆ ◆

. . . Is it possible I'll never see Nina again? Nina, an innocent eleven-year-old little girl—the victim of a stupid war. I feel sad. I cry and wonder why? She didn't do anything. A disgusting war has destroyed a young child's life.

◆ ◆ ◆

Zlata's Diary **133**

TAKE NOTES

Nonfiction

Cause-and-effect organization shows how one event leads to another event. List a cause and its effect from the bracketed passage.

_____

_____

_____

Build English Skills

An –s is added to the end of a verb to show that the action is happening at the present time. Circle the verbs in the second bracketed paragraph that have an –s to show what is happening now.

Nonfiction

The author controls the **mood** of a piece of writing with word choice. What mood does Zlata show with her choice of words in the underlined passage? Explain.

_____

_____

_____

Reading Check

Where do Zlata and her parents decide to sleep? Circle the answer in the text.

A full sentence needs a subject and a verb. Informal writing will sometimes have incomplete sentences. Read the underlined passage. Circle the subject of the second sentence. What verb is missing?

_____

Read the bracketed paragraph. Zlata reflects on the suffering in her life. How do you think writing a diary helps Zlata cope with the war?

_____

_____

_____

People in countries around the world celebrate birthdays in different ways. People in America often get birthday cakes with candles to share with friends and family. There is a candle on the cake for each year of a person's life. What traditions are there for birthdays in your native country?

_____

_____

She begins her letter of June 29 with words that have come to stand for her life, including despair, hunger, and fear.

♦ ♦ ♦

That's my life! The life of an innocent eleven-year-old schoolgirl!! A schoolgirl without a school, without the fun and excitement of school. A child without games, without friends, without the sun, without birds, without nature, without fruit, without chocolate or sweets, with just a little powdered milk. In short, a child without a childhood. A wartime child. I now realize that I am really living through a war, I am witnessing an ugly, disgusting war. I and thousands of other children in this town that is being destroyed, that is crying, weeping, seeking help, but getting none.

♦ ♦ ♦

She wonders if this terrible time will ever end.

♦ ♦ ♦

. . . I once heard that childhood is the most wonderful time of your life. And it is. I loved it, and now an ugly war is taking it all away from me.

♦ ♦ ♦

In her next letter she reports that her mother has been given a chance to move to Holland. Her mother doesn't know what to do. She and Zlata would be safe if they left. They would have to leave Zlata's father behind. On November 2, she writes that her mother has decided that she and Zlata must go. Perhaps Zlata's father will be able to go, too.

♦ ♦ ♦

Thursday, December 3, 1992

Dear Mimmy,
Today is my birthday. My first wartime birthday. Twelve years old. Congratulations. Happy birthday to me!

♦ ♦ ♦

Despite the war, her birthday was filled with kisses, presents, a family party, and even a birthday cake.

◆ ◆ ◆

. . . Not how it used to be, but there's a war on. Luckily there was no shooting, so we could celebrate.

It was nice, but something was missing. It's called peace!

◆ ◆ ◆

Her next entry from July 27, 1993, says that news reporters from all over the world are interested in her diary. She's excited. But the shooting continues and life is hard. There is no electricity, water, or gas, and very little food.

Finally, on October 7, she writes that things are getting back to normal. The shooting seems to have stopped. She is going to school again. But winter is coming and there is no heat in her apartment. She realizes that the war has now lasted for two terrible years. There is very little food.

Her letter of October 12 is a happy one. Her school had a pen pal program. She wrote a letter to a student in the United States. She is happy to report that she has received a reply—from a boy named Brandon who lives in Pennsylvania.

◆ ◆ ◆

. . . I now have a friend in America, and Brandon has a friend in Sarajevo. This is my first letter from across the Atlantic. And in it is a reply envelope, and a lovely pencil.

A Canadian TV crew and <u>journalist</u> from The Sunday Times (Janine) came to our gym class today. They brought me two chocolate bars.

Vocabulary Development

journalist (JER nuh list) *n.*   a person who writes reports for newspapers, magazines, television, or radio

TAKE NOTES

Nonfiction

Every author has a different writing style. An **author's style** might be formal or informal. A formal style is usually precise and has perfect grammar. An informal style is similar to how friends talk to one another. Is Zlata's writing style formal or informal in the bracketed passage? Explain.

_____

_____

Nonfiction

Compare-and-contrast organization shows how two or more things are the same or different. Seven months have passed between Zlata's birthday and her next diary entry. How does Zlata's life in the July entry differ from her life in the 1992 entry?

_____

_____

How is it the same?

_____

_____

Reading Check

Read about the October 7 entry. What does Zlata say is missing from her life? Circle the answer in the text.

Reflective writing is about an event in a writer's life. The writer looks back at important events in his or her life. What does Zlata reflect, or look back, on in her last diary entry?

_____

_____

Stop to Reflect

What might the author mean by "darkness" and "light" in the underlined sentence?

_____

_____

_____

Vocabulary and Pronunciation

The word *bathing* can mean "washing your whole body" or "being lit by a particular kind of light." Read the second under-lined sentence. Which meaning is used in this sentence?

_____

Reading Check

What is now behind Zlata and her family? Circle the answer in the text.

What a treat. It's been a long time since I've had sweets.

◆　◆　◆

In December 1993, Zlata begins her letter with a happy announcement. She is in Paris, France! There is electricity, water, gas, and food. She loves the "normal" things she sees, and the bright city lights. She feels as if she must be dreaming, or perhaps she is crazy!

◆　◆　◆

. . . The darkness is behind us; now we're bathed in light lit by good people. Remember that—good people. Bulb by bulb, not candles, but bulb by bulb, and me bathing in the lights of Paris. Yes, Paris. Incredible. You don't understand. You know, I don't think I understand either. I feel as though I must be crazy, dreaming, as though it's a fairy tale, but it's all TRUE.

Nonfiction

1. **Infer:** The war was hard for Zlata. How did the difficulties during the war change Zlata's life?

   _____

   _____

   _____

2. **Analyze Cause and Effect:** Zlata wanted to leave her home. However, she also wanted to stay. Why did Zlata have mixed feelings about leaving Sarajevo?

   _____

   _____

   _____

3. **Infer:** Writing in a diary is like writing to yourself. Do Mimmy and Zlata have the same personality? Support your answer.

   _____

   _____

   _____

4. **Narrative writing** is writing about real-life experiences. **Descriptive writing** is writing about things that appeal to the five senses. Fill in the chart below with examples of **nonfiction** writing in the diary.

Examples of Nonfiction Writing	
Narration	
Description	

RESEARCH THE AUTHOR

Biographical Sketch

- Search the Internet for information about Zlata in Paris. Use words and phrases such as "Zlata Filipović Paris." Look for Web sites that tell specifically about Paris. Look for an e-mail address so that you can write directly to Zlata. You might ask her questions for information that you have not been able to find in your research.

What I learned: _____

_____

_____

- Search the library for books about and by Zlata. Look for information about what it was like for Zlata to live in another country while her own was at war. Look for details about what she was able to do in Paris that she was not able to do in Bosnia.

What I learned: _____

_____

_____

- Watch the video interview with Zlata Filipović. Review your source material. Use this information to answer the following questions.

1. What do you think is important about what Zlata Filipović has done?

_____

_____

_____

2. How has the author's interest in journalism influenced her work?

_____

_____

_____

Hard as Nails • Water

READING SKILL

An **author's purpose** is the main reason the author writes a work. An author can have more than one purpose. An author may write an article about trees to give information about fir trees. The author might also want to persuade readers to protect fir trees.

Learn to recognize details that show you the author's purpose.

- Facts and statistics are used to give information or to convince a reader to take action or have a certain opinion.

- Stories about experiences are used to entertain readers.

- Opinions and thoughts are used to reflect on an experience.

Use this chart to help you determine an author's purpose.

Types of Details

↓

Author's Purpose

LITERARY ANALYSIS

A true story of real events and real people is a **narrative essay**. An author writes an **autobiographical narrative** to tell about an event that happened to him or her. The author may include his or her thoughts, feelings, or reactions.

Authors use specific details to achieve a purpose, such as sharing lessons they have learned from mistakes they have made.

Hard as Nails

Russell Baker

Summary Russell Baker is hired on his twelfth birthday to deliver newspapers in Baltimore. His boss, Mr. Deems, makes him work hard. Deems gives the newsboys a tour of the newsroom of the *Baltimore News-Post*. Russell dreams of having an important job at the newspaper. Later Russell remembers Deems as "hard as nails."

Reading/Writing Connection

Complete these sentences about the ways people show that they are responsible.

1. Responsible people <u>undertake</u> _____.

2. Team members should <u>participate</u> _____.

3. Good students <u>contribute</u> _____.

Note-taking Guide

Use this chart to record important details from the story.

Who makes Russell get a job?	Russell's mother
Where does he deliver papers?	
What does Mr. Deems do to make Russell sell more papers?	
How does Russell feel when he visits the newsroom?	
Why does Russell think Mr. Deems quit?	

Hard as Nails

1. **Respond:** Would you like to work for Deems? Explain your reasons.

_____

_____

_____

2. **Evaluate:** Think about how Deems treats the newsboys. Is Deems fair or unfair to them? Explain.

_____

_____

3. **Reading Skill:** The purpose is the main reason an author writes a work. List one **purpose** Baker may have had for writing this narrative essay.

_____

_____

4. **Literary Analysis:** Authors sometimes include specific details to explain why a person does something. Complete this chart to think about why Baker includes a particular event in his **autobiographical narrative**.

Event From Narrative	Author's Thoughts and Feelings	Why Is It Included?
Baker goes to the banquet.		

SUPPORT FOR WRITING AND EXTEND YOUR LEARNING

Writing: Letter

Imagine that you are Russell Baker. Write a **letter** to Deems. Follow these steps:

- List one of Deems's actions toward Russell and the newsboys.

  _____

  _____

- Describe how Russell felt about Deems at the time.

  _____

  _____

- Tell what Russell learned from Deems's action.

  _____

  _____

Use your notes to write a letter to Deems.

Research and Technology: Project

Prepare a **project** about a job in print journalism. Complete this chart for the job that you choose to research.

Job:			
What This Person Does	**Training or Education Needed**	**Salary**	**Source(s) of Information**

Water

Helen Keller

Summary Helen Keller was blind and deaf. Her new teacher, Anne Sullivan, tried to teach Helen how to communicate. Helen did not understand. The teacher ran water over Helen's hand one day. Miss Sullivan then spelled "w-a-t-e-r" in Helen's other hand. Helen connected the word to the thing she felt. Helen wanted to learn more words.

Reading/Writing Connection

Complete these sentences about a time when you found a new way to solve a problem.

1. It is important to <u>utilize</u> _____.

2. <u>Investigate</u> different solutions to find _____.

3. To <u>resolve</u> a difficult problem feels _____.

Note-taking Guide

Use this chart to record details from the story.

What did Miss Sullivan give Helen when she first arrived?	Miss Sullivan gave Helen a doll.
Why did Helen break the doll?	
How did Miss Sullivan teach Helen the word *water*?	
How did Helen feel after she learned her first word?	

Think of a time when you felt upset because you could not understand something. Describe how you felt when you finally understood it.

_____

_____

_____

A **narrative essay** is a true story about real events. Is this a narrative essay? How do you know?

_____

_____

The bracketed passage says that Helen did not understand the words she spelled. To better understand the paragraph, break the long sentence into shorter sentences.

I did not know that I was

_____

I did not even know that

_____

I was simply making

_____

_____

Water

Helen Keller

Try to imagine what it would be like to be both blind and deaf at the same time. The world around you would be completely dark and silent. It would be very hard to understand anything or to communicate with another person. This is the kind of world that young Helen Keller lives in, and there doesn't seem to be much hope for her. But her teacher Miss Sullivan is determined to help her. And one day she finds a new way for Helen to connect to the world around her.

As the story opens, Helen describes her first experiences with Miss Sullivan, her new teacher:

◆ ◆ ◆

The morning after my teacher came she led me into her room and gave me a doll. . . . When I had played with it a little while, Miss Sullivan slowly spelled into my hand the word "d-o-l-l." I was at once interested in this finger play and tried to <u>imitate</u> it.

◆ ◆ ◆

Helen finally succeeds in making the letters correctly. She is filled with childish pride and runs to show her mother what she has learned.

◆ ◆ ◆

I did not know that I was spelling a word or even that words existed; I was simply making my fingers go in monkey-like imitation.

◆ ◆ ◆

In the days that follow, Helen learns to hand-spell many other words. One day

---

Vocabulary Development

imitate (IM uh tayt) *v.*   to copy the way someone else speaks, moves, or does something

---

Miss Sullivan keeps trying to get Helen to understand that "d-o-l-l" applies to her big rag doll as well as to her new doll. But Helen grows impatient at these attempts. She dashes her new doll on the floor, breaking it into pieces. Helen feels no sorrow or regret, just relief. Miss Sullivan then takes Helen outside into the warm sunshine.

◆ ◆ ◆

We walked down the path to the well-house, attracted by the fragrance of the honeysuckle with which it was covered. Some one was drawing water and my teacher placed my hand under the spout. As the cool stream gushed over one hand she spelled into the other the word *water*, first slowly, then rapidly. I stood still, my whole attention fixed upon the motions of her fingers. Suddenly I felt a misty consciousness as of something forgotten—a thrill of returning thought; and somehow the mystery of language was revealed to me. I knew then that "w-a-t-e-r" meant the wonderful cool something that was flowing over my hand.

I left the well-house eager to learn. Everything had a name, and each name gave birth to a new thought.

◆ ◆ ◆

Inside the house, Helen finds the broken pieces of her doll. For the first time she feels sorrow. That day Helen learns many new words, including *mother*, *father*, *sister*, and *teacher*.

◆ ◆ ◆

It would have been difficult to find a happier child than I was as I lay in my crib at the close of that eventful day and lived over the joys it had brought me, and for the first time longed for a new day to come.

Vocabulary Development

drawing (DRAW ing) *v.*   making flow
consciousness (KAHN shuhs nis) *n.*   awareness

TAKE NOTES

Reading Skill

An **author's purpose** may be to instruct, to entertain, to persuade, or to express ideas.

The bracketed paragraph describes Helen's feelings about her breakthrough experience. What do you think is her purpose for writing? Explain.

_____

_____

_____

Build English Skills

An adverb tells *where, when, in what way,* or to what extent something is done. Adverbs often end in *-ly.* Circle two other words in the bracketed paragraph that end in *-ly* and write their meaning here.

_____

_____

Culture Note

Before she taught Helen Keller, Anne Sullivan was a student at the Perkins School for the Blind. It was the first school for the blind in the United States. Helen Keller became a student there in 1888.

Water

1. **Draw Conclusions:** Helen Keller learned the word *water*. What will Keller want to do when she wakes up the next day?

   _____

   _____

2. **Evaluate:** Why is it important to be able to communicate?

   _____

   _____

   _____

3. **Reading Skill:** An **author's purpose** is the main reason that the author writes a story. What is one purpose Keller may have had for writing this essay?

   _____

   _____

4. **Literary Analysis:** An **autobiographical narrative** tells about a certain time in an author's life. Complete this chart to figure out why Keller talks about a certain event in her autobiographical narrative.

Event From Narrative	Author's Thoughts and Feelings	Why Is It Included?
Helen connects the word *w-a-t-e-r* with water from the pump.		

SUPPORT FOR WRITING AND EXTEND YOUR LEARNING

Writing: Letter

Write a **letter** to the director of the school for the blind as Anne Sullivan. Use the following questions to write notes for your letter:

- How do you think Sullivan felt about Helen Keller before she learned words?

  _____

  _____

- How did Sullivan teach Keller what *w-a-t-e-r* means?

  _____

  _____

- How do you think Sullivan feels about what happened?

  _____

  _____

Listening and Speaking: Presentation

Prepare a **presentation** for young children about Helen Keller. Use this chart to help you get started.

What was Helen like before she learned words?	
Why was learning language so exciting for Helen?	
What can you learn from Helen's story?	

The Shutout • Jackie Robinson: Justice at Last

READING SKILL

An **author's purpose** is his or her reason for writing. **Ask questions** to figure out the author's purpose.

- What kinds of details am I given?

- How are the details given?

- Why does the author give these details in this way?

The chart shows the answers to these questions for two different works about building a doghouse. The answers show that each work has a different purpose. Fill in the empty space with details from the story as you read.

What Kinds of Details?		
Directions for building a doghouse	Author tries to build a doghouse	
How Presented?		
Numbered steps	Exaggerated stories	
Why?		
To make the directions easy to follow	To make the situation funny	
Purpose		
To inform	To entertain	

LITERARY ANALYSIS

An **essay** is a short piece of nonfiction. An **expository essay** gives information, discusses ideas and opinions, and explains how to do or make something.

The Shutout

Patricia C. McKissack and Frederick McKissack, Jr.

Summary This essay describes baseball's early history. At first, African Americans played on teams of black and white players. Baseball became a business after the Civil War. African American players were "shut out" from playing on major league teams until after World War II. They formed their own teams as a result.

Reading/Writing Connection

Complete these sentences to describe what a person should do when faced with an unfair situation.

1. Those who are treated unfairly should <u>confront</u> _____.

2. Keep trying to <u>prevail</u> against _____.

3. Always <u>pursue</u> _____ even when things seem hard.

Note-taking Guide

Fill in the dates on the chart to create a timeline of the history of baseball.

Event	Baseball started becoming popular.	The National Association of Base Ball Players was formed.	South Carolina seceded from the Union.	The National Association of Base Ball Players voted not to admit teams with African American members.
Date				

The Shutout

1. **Respond:** Asking questions can help you understand a piece of writing. Think of one or two questions you have about the essay. Write your questions in the first column of the chart below. Then, look for details in the essay that answer your questions. Write an answer to each question in the second column. Explain in the third column how the answers help you understand the essay.

Questions	Answers	Has Understanding Changed? Explain:

2. **Cause and Effect:** African Americans were not allowed to play on major league teams at one time. What effect did this have on the history of baseball?

_____

_____

3. **Reading Skill:** An **author's purpose** is his or her reason for writing. What is the purpose of the essay?

_____

_____

4. **Literary Analysis:** This essay focuses on one part of baseball's history. What is the focus of this **expository essay**?

_____

_____

SUPPORT FOR WRITING AND EXTEND YOUR LEARNING

Writing: Persuasive Letter

Write a **persuasive letter** to a friend, encouraging him or her to read "The Shutout." Focus on the following questions:

- What is the main idea of the essay?

  _____

- What specific details from the essay will persuade your friend to read it?

  _____

  _____

- Why do you want your friend to read the essay?

  _____

  _____

Use your notes to write the persuasive letter.

Listening and Speaking: Give Directions

Prepare a presentation for younger students that **gives directions** on how to perform certain baseball moves. Take notes in this chart.

Steps to Follow:			
Swing a Bat	**Steal a Base**	**Set Up a Double Play**	**Bunt**

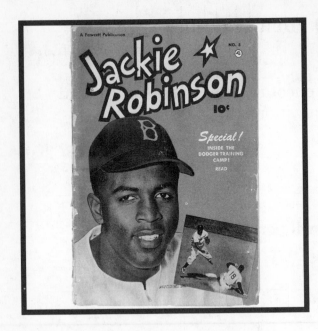

Jackie Robinson: Justice at Last

Geoffrey C. Ward and Ken Burns

Summary Branch Rickey owned the Dodgers baseball team. He wanted African Americans to play major league baseball. He asked Jackie Robinson to become the first black player on his team. Robinson faced many obstacles and challenges. He became a role model.

Reading/Writing Connection

Complete these sentences about problems you might face as you try to reach an important goal.

1. It is best to <u>confront</u> a problem _____.

2. To reach a goal, some people must <u>contend</u> with _____.

3. When an unexpected problem happens, <u>proceed</u> _____.

Note-taking Guide

Use the chart to recall the most important details of the story.

Who was Branch Rickey?	He was the owner of the Dodgers.
Why does he want Jackie Robinson on his team?	
What problems did Robinson have during his first season?	
Why was it important that Robinson not fight back?	

Jackie Robinson: Justice at Last
Geoffrey C. Ward and Ken Burns

Professional baseball in the United States was for whites only until Branch Rickey hired Jackie Robinson. Because he is the first black major league baseball player, Robinson must rise above the insults hurled at him. He must prove by his play that he belongs on the Brooklyn Dodgers and that other African American athletes belong in the major leagues. He succeeds, and baseball teams become integrated.

As the story begins, Branch Rickey decides that the time has come for blacks and whites to play together.

◆ ◆ ◆

It was 1945, and World War II had ended. Americans of all races had died for their country. Yet black men were still not allowed in the major leagues. The national <u>pastime</u> was loved by all America, but the major leagues were for white men only.

Branch Rickey of the Brooklyn Dodgers thought that was wrong. He was the only team owner who believed blacks and whites should play together. Baseball, he felt, would become even more thrilling, and fans of all colors would swarm to his ballpark.

Rickey decided his team would be the first to <u>integrate</u>. There were plenty of brilliant Negro league players, but he knew the first black major leaguer would need much more than athletic ability.

◆ ◆ ◆

Vocabulary Development

pastime (PAS tym) *n.*   a way of spending spare time pleasantly

integrate (IN tuh grayt) *v.*   make available to people of all races on an equal basis

---

TAKE NOTES

Activate Prior Knowledge

Think about a person whose courage led to new opportunities for other people. Describe the person, and list his or her accomplishments.

_____

_____

_____

Reading Skill

Details can help you determine the **author's purpose**, or main reason for writing. Underline one important detail in the bracketed passage. Write a question you can ask to understand the authors' purpose.

_____

_____

_____

Culture Note

In the early 1900s, major league baseball did not allow African American players. Black players formed their own teams and organized the Negro leagues in the 1920s. Jackie Robinson began his professional baseball career on the Kansas City Monarchs, a Negro league team.

An **expository essay** is a short piece of nonfiction about a specific subject. What is the subject of this expository essay?

_____

_____

_____

Would you have accepted a place on the team if you had been Jackie Robinson? Why or why not?

_____

_____

_____

A dash (—) signals information that interrupts the flow of text. A dash is a longer and more forceful pause than a comma. Read the underlined sentences. Rewrite the sentences as 4 separate sentences without using dashes.

_____

_____

_____

_____

Many fans and players were prejudiced. The first black player would be cursed and booed. His own teammates might try to pick fights.

◆ ◆ ◆

But somehow this man had to rise above that. No matter what happened, he must never lose his temper. No matter what was said to him, he must never answer back. If he had even one fight, people might say integration would not work.

◆ ◆ ◆

Rickey thinks Robinson is the right man. He is 28, a superb athlete, and is college-educated. He hit .387 in his first season in the Negro leagues. He is the grandson of a slave and is proud of his race.

Robinson had always stood up for his rights. But Rickey tells him he will have to stop.

◆ ◆ ◆

At first Robinson thought Rickey wanted someone who was afraid to defend himself. But as they talked, he realized that in this case a truly brave man would have to avoid fighting. He thought for a while, then promised Rickey he would not fight back.

Robinson signed with the Dodgers and went to play in the minors in 1946. Rickey was right—fans insulted him, and so did players. But he performed brilliantly and avoided fights. Then, in 1947, he came to the majors.

◆ ◆ ◆

Many Dodgers were angry. Some signed a petition demanding to be traded.

◆ ◆ ◆

On April 15—Opening Day—26,623 fans came out to Ebbets Field. More than half of them were black—Robinson was already their hero. Now he was making history just by being on the field.

The afternoon was cold and wet, but no one left the ballpark. The Dodgers beat the Boston

Braves, 5–3. Robinson went hitless, but the hometown fans didn't seem to care—they cheered his every move.

◆ ◆ ◆

Robinson's first season was difficult. Fans threatened to kill him. Players tried to hurt him. The St. Louis Cardinals threatened to strike if he took the field. In some states Robinson couldn't eat or sleep in the same places as his teammates, because of laws separating the races.

◆ ◆ ◆

Yet through it all, he kept his promise to Rickey. No matter who insulted him, he never retaliated.

◆ ◆ ◆

Robinson's dignity paid off. Thousands of fans jammed stadiums to see him play. The Dodgers set attendance records.

◆ ◆ ◆

Slowly his teammates accepted him, realizing that he was the spark that made them a winning team. No one was more daring on the base paths or better with the glove. At the plate, he had great bat control—he could hit the ball anywhere. That season, he was named baseball's first Rookie of the Year.

Jackie Robinson went on to a glorious career. But he did more than play the game well—his bravery taught Americans a lesson. Branch Rickey opened a door, and Jackie Robinson stepped through it, making sure it could never be closed again. Something wonderful happened to baseball—and America—the day Jackie Robinson joined the Dodgers.

Vocabulary Development

retaliated (ri TAL ee ayt id) *v.* harmed or did wrong to someone in return for an injury or wrong he or she caused

---

TAKE NOTES

Vocabulary and Pronunciation

The suffix *–less* means "without." The word *hitless* means "without hits." In other words, Robinson did not get a hit in the ballgame. Tell what each of the following words means.

1. careless _____
2. thoughtless _____

Read Fluently

The underlined passage describes the way that Branch Rickey and Jackie Robinson changed baseball. To better understand the paragraph, break the long sentence into shorter sentences.

Branch Rickey _____

_____.

Jackie Robinson _____

_____.

They made sure _____

_____

_____.

Reading Check

What did the St. Louis Cardinals threaten to do? Underline the answer.

Jackie Robinson: Justice at Last

1. **Respond:** Fill out the chart below. Write a question you have about the essay in the first column. Write an answer to each question in the second column, using details from the essay. Explain in the third column how the answers affect your understanding of the essay.

Questions	Answers	Has Understanding Changed? Explain:
What difficulties did Robinson face in his first year?		

2. **Speculate:** Robinson's teammates eventually accepted him as a member of their team. Why did everyone else eventually accept Robinson and the integration of baseball?

_____

_____

3. **Reading Skill:** The **author's purpose** is his or her reason for writing. What is the **purpose** of this essay?

_____

_____

4. **Literary Analysis:** An **essay** is a short piece of nonfiction about a specific subject. What is the focus of this **expository essay**?

_____

_____

SUPPORT FOR WRITING AND EXTEND YOUR LEARNING

Writing: Persuasive Letter

Write a **persuasive letter** to a friend, encouraging him or her to read "Jackie Robinson: Justice at Last." Answer the following questions:

• What is the main idea of the essay?

_____

• What specific details from the essay will persuade your friend to read it?

_____

_____

• Why do you want your friend to read the essay?

_____

Use your answers to write your persuasive letter.

Research and Technology: Visual Timeline

Prepare a **visual timeline** to tell the story of Jackie Robinson's baseball career. Use information from the text to fill in the chart.

Date	Event in Jackie Robinson's Life
1919	year born
1942	enters U.S. Army
Early 1945	plays shortstop in the Negro League
1945	
1946	
April 15, 1947	
End-of-season, 1947	
1949	voted baseball's most valuable player
1957	retires from baseball
1962	inducted into Baseball Hall of Fame
1997	jersy number (42) retired from baseball

Persuasive Speeches

ABOUT PERSUASIVE SPEECHES

A **persuasive speech** is a public presentation that argues for or against a particular position. A good persuasive speech can change people's minds about an issue. Examples of persuasive speeches include campaign speeches and sermons. Persuasive speeches usually have the following characteristics:

- an issue with two sides (For example, the death penalty is an issue with two sides. Some people are for it, and other people are against it.)
- a clear statement of the speaker's purpose, or reason
- a clear statement of the speaker's position, or opinion
- clear organization of the text
- facts, statistics, and examples to support the position
- powerful language meant to persuade

READING SKILL

You should always **evaluate an author's argument**. Look for a clear statement of the author's argument. Pay attention to facts and other information that support the argument.

Use the checklist below to evaluate the following speech.

Checklist for Evaluating an Author's Argument
☐ Does the author present a clear argument?
☐ Is the argument supported by evidence?
☐ Is the evidence believable?
☐ Does the author use sound reasoning to develop the argument?
☐ Do I agree with the message? Why or why not?

Build Understanding
Knowing these words will help you read this speech.
desecration (des uh KRAY shuhn) *n.* the act of insulting something holy
heinous (HAY nus) *adj.* very wicked or evil

Preserving a Great American Symbol
Richard Durbin

Congressman Richard Durbin gave the following humorous speech in the House of Representatives on July 26, 1989. While most speeches to Congress are serious, Durbin's is humorous yet persuasive and "drives home" the point that wooden baseball bats should not be replaced with metal ones.

Mr. Speaker, I rise to condemn the desecration of a great American symbol. No, I am not referring to flagburning; I am referring to the baseball bat.

Several experts tell us that the wooden baseball bat is doomed to extinction, that major league baseball players will soon be standing at home plate with aluminum bats in their hands.

TAKE NOTES

Culture Note

Many people consider baseball the American national pastime. The game has been played since the middle of the 1800s. Some famous players include Babe Ruth and Lou Gehrig. What sport do you connect with your native country?

_____

_____

_____

Reading Persuasive Speeches

What is the topic of Durbin's speech? Circle the answer in the first paragraph of the speech.

Stop to Reflect

Think about how Durbin's audience might react to his jokes. Why might a speaker use humor in a **persuasive speech**?

_____

_____

_____

_____

Reading Check

What type of bat might replace the wooden baseball bat? Underline the answer.

A colon is often used to introduce items in a list. The text before the colon explains the list that is to follow. Read the bracketed paragraph. What are the items after the colon describing? Circle the answer in the text.

How does Durbin use humor to persuade and entertain in the bracketed paragraph?

_____

_____

_____

Look closely at the evidence that Durbin presents. Underline one piece of evidence he gives. **Evaluate** the evidence. Does Durbin use logical evidence to support his argument? Explain.

_____

_____

_____

Baseball fans have been forced to endure countless indignities by those who just cannot leave well enough alone: designated hitters,[1] plastic grass, uniforms that look like pajamas, chicken clowns dancing on the base lines, and, of course, the most heinous sacrilege, lights in Wrigley Field.[2]

Are we willing to hear the crack of a bat replaced by the dinky ping? Are we ready to see the Louisville Slugger replaced by the aluminum ping dinger? Is nothing sacred?

Please do not tell me that wooden bats are too expensive, when players who cannot hit their weight are being paid more money than the President of the United States.

Please do not try to sell me on the notion that these metal clubs will make better hitters.

What will be next? Teflon baseballs? Radar-enhanced gloves? I ask you.

I do not want to hear about saving trees. Any tree in America would gladly give its life for the glory of a day at home plate.

I do not know if it will take a constitutional amendment to keep our baseball traditions alive, but if we forsake the great Americana of broken-bat singles and pine tar,[3] we will have certainly lost our way as a nation.

---

1. **designated hitter** player who bats in place of the pitcher and does not play a defensive position. The position was created in 1973 in the American League. Some fans argue that it has changed the game for the worse.
2. **Wrigley Field** historic baseball field in Chicago. It did not have lights for night games until 1988. Some fans regretted the change.
3. **broken-bat singles . . . pine tar** When a batter breaks a wooden bat while hitting the ball and makes it to first base, it is a notable event in a baseball game. Pine tar is a substance used to improve the batter's grip on a wooden bat.

THINKING ABOUT THE PERSUASIVE SPEECH

1. Identify the author's purpose in delivering this speech.

   _____

   _____

2. How does the author's use of humorous images and language appeal to his audience's emotions?

   _____

   _____

READING SKILL

3. Does the sentence "Metal bats should not replace wooden ones" state the position of the author in this speech?

   _____

   _____

4. Does the statement "Baseball players make too much money" support the author's argument? Explain.

   _____

   _____

TIMED WRITING: RESPONSE (20 minutes)

Respond to the speech "Preserving a Great American Symbol."
- Do you agree or disagree with Durbin's argument?

   _____

- List at least two details from the speech that support your argument.

   _____

   _____

Langston Terrace • Turkeys

READING SKILL

The **main idea** is the major point in a literary work. Sometimes the author states the main idea. Other times, you must figure it out by **identifying key details**. Key details can tell you what a work is about. They are sometimes repeated throughout a literary work. Key details are related to other details in a work.

Record key details in the graphic organizer as you read. Then, use those details to figure out the main idea.

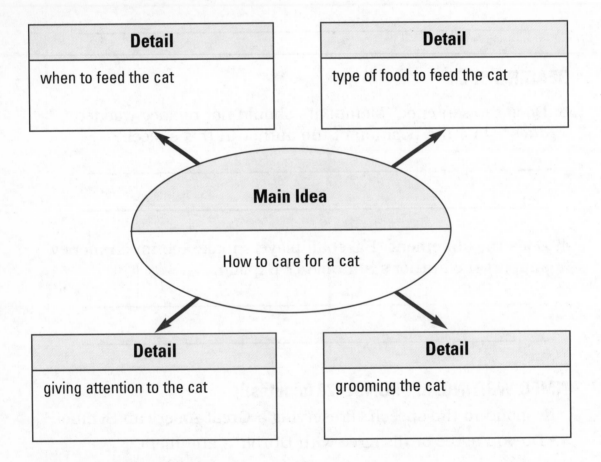

Detail

when to feed the cat

Detail

type of food to feed the cat

Main Idea

How to care for a cat

Detail

giving attention to the cat

Detail

grooming the cat

LITERARY ANALYSIS

An **author's influences** are the cultural ideas and historical events that affect his or her writing. Look for details about the author's influences as you read. They may include the time and place of the author's birth, the author's cultural background, or world events.

Langston Terrace

Eloise Greenfield

Summary Eloise Greenfield and her family move to a new house in Langston Terrace. Langston Terrace is a new, low-rent housing project in Washington, D.C. The people who live there start music, sports, and poetry programs. Eloise and her friends have pleasant memories of Langston Terrace.

Reading/Writing Connection

Complete these sentences about things that are needed to make a community.

1. One way to <u>establish</u> a new community is _____.

2. Community members <u>participate</u> _____.

3. A group of people must <u>reside</u> _____.

Note-taking Guide

Use this chart to record important details from the story.

What is Langston Terrace?	A low-rent housing project
Where is it?	
How does Eloise's family get a house there?	
Why does Eloise have good memories of Langston Terrace?	

Langston Terrace

1. **Compare and Contrast:** Eloise's family lived with relatives and friends before they moved to Langston Terrace. How is the family's new home like their old home? How is it different?

_____

_____

_____

2. **Speculate:** Why might people who used to live at Langston Terrace want to have a reunion? Explain.

_____

_____

3. **Reading Skill:** The main idea is the major point in a literary work. In your own words, state the **main idea** of the essay.

_____

_____

4. **Literary Analysis:** Think about when and where "Langston Terrace" takes place. Use the chart to list cultural and historical factors that may have **influenced** Greenfield.

Time and Place	Cultural Background	World Events

SUPPORT FOR WRITING AND EXTEND YOUR LEARNING

Writing: Journal Entry

Write a **journal entry** as if you were a young Eloise Greenfield. Choose an event from the essay. Focus on these questions:

• What do you remember about this event?

_____

_____

_____

• Why does this event stand out in your mind?

_____

_____

_____

Use your notes to write the journal entry.

Listening and Speaking: Dramatic Reading

Perform a **dramatic reading** of the last two paragraphs of "Langston Terrace." Use the chart to record your thoughts about your presentation. Be sure to note what you could do to communicate meaning.

	Comments
How should you use your voice?	
Where should you pause to stress an important point?	
Describe the body language you should use.	

Turkeys

Bailey White

Summary Bailey White's mother was a friend to local ornithologists, or people who study birds. The ornithologists found a wild turkey nest that was not watched over by a mother turkey. The ornithologists needed to keep the turkey eggs warm. Bailey's illness helped the ornithologists save the turkey eggs.

Reading/Writing Connection

Complete these sentences to describe ways to connect with nature.

1. Nature can <u>evoke</u> feelings of _____.

2. Spending time outdoors can <u>affect</u> _____.

3. One way to connect with nature is to <u>focus</u> on _____.

Note-taking Guide

Use the chart to record important details from the story.

Who is the narrator?	The narrator is Bailey White when she was a child.
What are the ornithologists studying?	
Why does the mother turkey leave the nest?	
How do the ornithologists save the turkey eggs?	

Turkeys
Bailey White

Something about my mother attracts ornithologists. It all started years ago when a couple of them discovered she had a rare species of woodpecker coming to her bird feeder. They came in the house and sat around the window, exclaiming and taking pictures with big fancy cameras. But long after the red cockaded woodpeckers had gone to roost, the ornithologists were still there. . . .

♦ ♦ ♦

The ornithologists were worried about wild turkeys in the area. Wild turkeys had begun to <u>breed</u> with farmers' domestic turkeys. This was causing the species to become weaker. They could not fly as well as they once could.

♦ ♦ ♦

It was during that time, the spring when I was six years old, that I caught the measles. I had a high fever, and my mother was worried about me. She kept the house quiet and dark and crept around silently, trying different <u>methods</u> of cooling me down.

Even the ornithologists stayed away—but not out of fear of the measles. . . . The fact was, they had discovered a wild turkey nest.

♦ ♦ ♦

<u>The ornithologists were watching over the nest, protecting it from predators.</u> One night, they came to the narrator's house while she was still sick. They carried a cardboard box. Half asleep, she could hear them talking above her.

♦ ♦ ♦

Vocabulary Development

breed (breed) *v.*   have babies

methods (METH uhdz) *n.*   ways of doing something

Activate Prior Knowledge

Have you or has someone you know ever helped a wild animal? What did you or the other person do?

_____

_____

Literary Analysis

An **author's influences** are the places, cultural ideas, and historic events that affect his or her writing. Explain how the place where White grew up **influenced** the writing of this essay.

_____

_____

_____

Read Fluently

Pronouns such as *he, she, they, them,* and *it* are used in place of a noun. A pronoun can be used instead of repeating a name or word. Look at the underlined sentence. What noun does the pronoun *it* replace?

_____

Reading Check

What illness did the narrator have? Circle the answer.

Reading Skill

Read the first bracketed passage. **Key details** can help you figure out the **main idea** of an essay. What key detail is important to the ornithologists' plan?

_____

_____

Build English Skills

Most verbs in English add –ed to form the past tense. Verbs that do not are called irregular verbs. For example, *came* is the past tense of the irregular verb *come*. Underline in the second bracketed paragraph the irregular past tense forms of the verbs *run, take off,* and *say.*

Reading Check

What did the narrator find in her bed? Underline the answer.

The next morning I was better. . . . The memory of the ornithologists with their whispered voices was like a dream from another life. But when I pulled down the covers, there staring up at me with googly eyes and wide mouths were sixteen fuzzy baby turkeys, and the cracked chips and caps of sixteen brown speckled eggs.

◆ ◆ ◆

It turned out the mother turkey had abandoned her nest. It was a cold night and the eggs had to be kept warm. Remembering the narrator's fever, the ornithologists brought them there.

The baby turkeys grew stronger. They followed the narrator everywhere she went.

◆ ◆ ◆

Finally, in late summer, the day came when they were ready to fly for the first time as adult birds. The ornithologists gathered. I ran down the hill, and the turkeys ran too. Then, one by one, they took off. They flew high and fast. The ornithologists . . . smiled. They jumped up and down and hugged each other. "One hundred percent pure wild turkey!" they said.

Nearly forty years have passed since then. Now there's a vaccine for measles. And the woods where I live are full of pure wild turkeys. . . .

Vocabulary Development

vaccine (vak SEEN) *n.* a substance used to protect people from a disease; it contains a weak form of the virus that causes the disease

Turkeys

1. **Evaluate:** Why is the author's fever important to the ornithologists?

   _____

   _____

2. **Interpret:** How do you think the author feels when she watches the turkeys take off? Explain.

   _____

   _____

   _____

3. **Reading Skill:** The **main idea** is the most important point the author makes. State the main idea of this essay in your own words.

   _____

   _____

   _____

4. **Literary Analysis:** Use this chart to list cultural factors that may have **influenced** the author when she was writing "Turkeys." All of the information you need is in the essay.

Time and Place	Cultural Background	World Events
		Wild turkeys were facing extinction in the area.

SUPPORT FOR WRITING AND EXTEND YOUR LEARNING

Writing: Journal Entry

Write a **journal entry** as if you were Bailey White as a child. Focus on the following questions:

- Which event will you write about? Describe what happened.

_____

_____

_____

- What did White say about the event in the essay? Explain why this event was important to White.

_____

_____

_____

Use your notes to write the journal entry.

Research and Technology: Presentation

Prepare a **presentation** on conservation. First, choose the conservation topic you will research. Focus on the following questions as you research your topic:

- What topic do you want to focus on?

_____

- Why is this topic important?

_____

_____

- What message do you want to bring to your audience?

_____

_____

Magazine Articles

ABOUT MAGAZINE ARTICLES

A **magazine** is a periodical. A periodical is a collection of articles or stories published at regular time periods. Periodicals are usually published once a week or once a month.

The articles in magazines focus on topics that are timely. To be timely means to be of interest to people at the time the magazine is published. Magazine articles usually contain:

- pictures and graphics
- headings to break up text
- an interesting title that captures readers' attention

READING SKILL

An **author's purpose** is his or her main reason for writing. Authors of magazine articles write for one or more of these purposes:

- to inform readers
- to state a viewpoint or opinion
- to persuade readers to take a certain action
- to entertain readers

Look for details and language in the text that indicate the author's purpose. Decide whether the author has successfully achieved that purpose. Use this chart to list details and language that will help you **recognize and evaluate an author's purpose.**

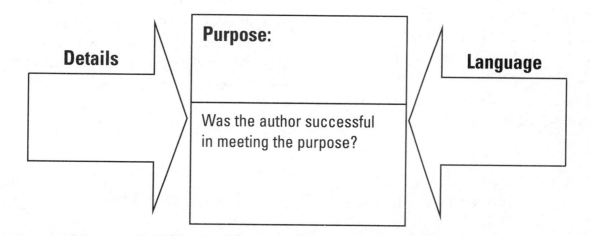

Details

Purpose:

Was the author successful in meeting the purpose?

Language

Where Do Turkeys Go After Being Pardoned by the President?

Bijal P. Trivedi

Presidential turkeys spend their entire life bettering themselves in anticipation of that glorious presidential pardon; that ethereal moment when they are forever reprieved from the roasting rack. It all begins in April when about 2,500 toms hatch from their shell. These turkeys, already a notch above the common variety destined for the dinner plate, are raised in an airconditioned barn with fluffy piles of sawdust up to their knees, said National Turkey Federation Chairman Nick Weaver.

In August, when the toms have reached about 25 pounds (11 kilograms), six are chosen as presidential candidates. Weaver, as chairman of the NTF, will raise and choose the final pair of birds destined for the appointment at the White House.

Birds Chosen for Looks

These six elite specimens, chosen for their fine plumage, poise and portly figure, are moved to a separate building where they are groomed for their future executive tasks.

From August through November and up until the day before the pardon, the goal is to familiarize the birds with people so that they don't lose their composure during the ceremony with the President.

Weaver came up with a particularly unique way to do this. The six birds are exposed to people dressed in longsleeved, dark-blue overalls to simulate the dark-blue suits of the officials and security personnel present at the White House.

November 20, 2001 • *National Geographic Today*

This year Weaver chose the presidential and vice presidential turkeys from the half dozen eager toms in Goldsboro, North Carolina, two days before the ceremony in the nation's capital.

Weaver chose the tom he thought was the "most regal"—the bird with the most beautiful white plumage, the best behavior and poise. The First Bird, Liberty, and his backup, Freedom, were placed in crates and driven to Washington.

The Good Life

For the presidential pair, their road trip to the White House is where the good life begins. The birds spend the night before the White House ceremony at the Hotel Washington, a plush establishment with a terrace restaurant that overlooks the President's mansion. The unlikely guests spend the night on the terrace level in a service corridor.

What the President Said

After leaving the Hotel Washington the birds were whisked to the White House Rose Garden. When the President appeared, Liberty was hoisted onto a pedestal.

"I'm not going to speak too long, because our guest of honor looks a little nervous," said Bush. "Nobody's told him yet that I'm going to give him a pardon."

Then the pardon: "For this turkey and his traveling companion, this will not be their last Thanksgiving," said the President. "By virtue of an unconditional presidential pardon, they are safe from harm."

He then invited the children to pet Liberty. Within a couple of minutes of pardoning the turkey, a few turkey embraces, and a few autographs, the President hurried back inside the White House.

For Liberty it was the pinnacle of a career. Liberty and Freedom were whisked off to Frying Pan Park's Kidwell Farm in Herndon, Virginia—about 30 minutes west of Washington—where the pardoned turkeys live.

November 20, 2001 • *National Geographic Today*

THINKING ABOUT THE MAGAZINE ARTICLE

1. This article entertains readers. What other purpose might someone have for reading this article?

_____

2. What is the purpose of pardoning the turkey?

_____

READING SKILL

3. Which purpose does the following sentence suggest? "Presidential turkeys spend their entire life bettering themselves in anticipation of that glorious presidential pardon."

_____

4. What is your first clue that this is a humorous article?

_____

TIMED WRITING: EXPLANATION (20 minutes)

Explain at least three ways that the author uses humor to entertain readers.

• Reread the article. List words or sentences that make you smile or laugh. Explain why these details are funny.

_____

_____

• Pick three of the best examples to write about in your explanation. Explain what you find funny about each one.

_____

_____

_____

La Leña Buena • from The Pigman & Me

READING SKILL

The **main idea** is the most important point in a story or essay. You need to be able to **distinguish between important and unimportant details** to find the main idea. Important details are small pieces of information. They tell more about the main idea. They are also called *supporting details.*

- Ask yourself questions such as these about details in a piece of writing: *Why did the author include this detail? Does this detail help readers understand the main idea of the work?*

- Remember that not all details support the main idea.

Use this chart to list details as you read. Decide whether the details are important. Then, use the important details to write the main idea.

Detail	Important?
Tío Abrán earns a living making charcoal from wood.	Yes
Main Idea:	

LITERARY ANALYSIS

Mood is the overall feeling a story or an essay creates in a reader. For example, the mood of a piece may be happy, sad, scary, or hopeful. Writers carefully choose words and word pictures that appeal to the reader's senses. They help create a mood in their stories.

Some writing creates one mood throughout the whole selection. In other pieces, the mood changes.

La Leña Buena

John Phillip Santos

Summary The narrator tells the story of his great-grandfather's brother, Tío Abrán. Tío Abrán made a successful living from wood in Mexico. He could tell the best way to use the wood from different trees. Tío Abrán had to deal with Mexican revolutionaries before coming to America.

Reading/Writing Connection

Complete each sentence to explain how young people benefit from stories about their older family members.

1. It is often possible to <u>benefit</u> from _____.

2. Her grandmother's stories <u>enriched</u> her _____.

3. Paying attention to _____ can <u>enable</u>

   people to avoid making some mistakes.

Note-taking Guide

Use this chart to record three important details from "La Leña Buena."

Important Detail	Important Detail	Important Detail
1. Tío Abrán knows a lot about wood.	2.	3.

La Leña Buena
John Phillip Santos

Tío Abrán knew the traits of wood. Huisache burns fast. It does not give off lots of heat. Huisache is not good for home fires. Mesquite and cedar are great for home fires. They burn slowly. They also give off lots of heat. They make excellent charcoal. Tío Abrán made charcoal. People in Mexico respected the charcoal he made. Its fire burned a long time.

Tío Abrán brought his family to the United States around 1920. He was one of the last members of the Garcia family to leave Mexico. He could not find good wood for making charcoal in Mexico. He had to travel far from his home to find mesquite. He also had to travel through places where there were people who wanted to fight.

◆ ◆ ◆

. . . Out by the old Villa las Rusias, in a valley far off the road, there were mesquite trees in every direction as far as you could see. He made an arrangement with the owner of the villas to give him a cut from the sale of charcoal he made from the mesquite. But many times, the revolucionarios confiscated his day's load of wood, leaving him to return home, humiliated, with an empty wagon.

◆ ◆ ◆

Tío Abrán was reluctant to leave Mexico. He brought his family to San Antonio. He told Abuelo Jacobo that he would have stayed in Mexico if it were easier to get mesquite.

Vocabulary Development

cut (kut) *n.*   someone's share of something, such as money
confiscated (KAHN fuhs kayt id) *v.*   seized, usually by governmental authority
humiliated (hyoo MIL ee ayt id) *v.*   ashamed or embarrassed

---

TAKE NOTES

Activate Prior Knowledge

Think about something you do very well. How would it feel if other people made it difficult for you to do this activity?

_____

_____

Read Fluently

A **pronoun** is a word that stands for a noun or for a word that takes the place of a noun. Underline *it, he* and *they* in the first bracketed paragraph. Then circle the nouns that they replace in this passage.

Literary Analysis

Mood is the overall feeling a literary work produces in a reader. Read the second bracketed passage. What **mood**, or feeling, is created in this paragraph?

_____

_____

Reading Skill

Important details are small pieces of information that tell more about the **main idea**. List one important detail that supports the main idea that trees are important in Tío Abrán's life.

_____

_____

La Leña Buena

1. **Interpret:** Tío Abrán made charcoal from trees. Why did Tío Abrán decide to leave Mexico?

   _____

   _____

   _____

2. **Infer:** Tío Abrán said that he would have stayed in Mexico if mesquite were easier to get. What does this comment tell you about his feelings toward Mexico?

   _____

   _____

3. **Reading Skill:** What is the **main idea** of this essay?

   _____

   _____

4. **Literary Analysis:** Complete this chart to show one word and one image that help create the **mood** in "La Leña Buena."

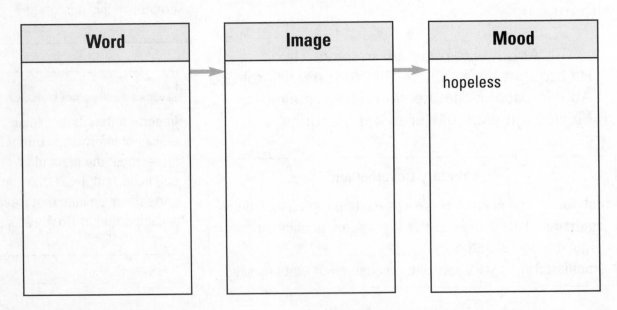

Word	Image	Mood
		hopeless

SUPPORT FOR WRITING AND EXTEND YOUR LEARNING

Writing: Problem-and-Solution Essay

Write a **problem-and-solution essay** to help immigrants adjust to life in the United States. A problem-and-solution essay includes possible solutions to a problem. Use the following chart to help you brainstorm ideas for your essay.

1. Describe the problem.	
2. Describe the solution.	
3. Why will this solution work?	

Research and Technology: Annotated Bibliography Entries

Use the library or the Internet to learn more about twenty-first-century immigration to the United States. Write **annotated bibliography entries** for at least two of your sources. Answer these questions to help you write your entries.

- Who is the author of this information? _____

- What is the title? _____

- Who is the publisher of the source? _____

- When was the source published? _____

- What city was the source published in? _____

- Why is this a good source of information? _____

_____

from The Pigman & Me

Paul Zindel

Summary Paul Zindel is the new kid at school. He does not know the rules yet. He accidentally gives John Quinn a black eye. John wants to fight Paul. Paul asks Nonno Frankie for advice about fighting. Paul tries to follow the advice during the fight. The fight does not end the way he expected.

Reading/Writing Connection

Complete the paragraph to describe a rule that is important at school, at the library, or in your home.

One rule that everyone can <u>benefit</u> from following is _____

_____. Following this rule will <u>enable</u> everyone

to _____. We can <u>contribute</u> by _____.

Note-taking Guide

Use this chart to record important events from the story.

What does Richard Cahill forget to tell Paul?	What does Paul do to John Quinn?	What does Nonno Frankie teach Paul?	Who saves Paul at the end?
Richard forgets to tell Paul that he can only have a paddle for fifteen minutes.			

from The Pigman & Me

1. **Infer:** Paul pretends to be hurt when he falls during the fight. Why does Paul act as though he is hurt?

   _____

2. **Compare and Contrast:** Think about how John acts when Paul falls down. Think about how Moose acts. How is John's behavior different from Moose's behavior?

   _____

   _____

3. **Reading Skill:** The **main idea** is the most important point in a literary work. What is the main idea of this selection?

   _____

   _____

4. **Reading Skill:** What is one **important detail** that supports the main idea?

   _____

5. **Literary Analysis:** Authors use words and images to create a **mood**. Part of this selection is tense and suspenseful. Complete the chart to analyze which words and images create the mood of this selection.

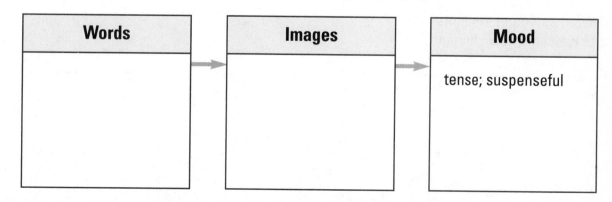

Words	Images	Mood
		tense; suspenseful

SUPPORT FOR WRITING AND EXTEND YOUR LEARNING

Writing: Problem-and-Solution Essay

Write a **problem-and-solution essay** to help new students adjust to one feature of life at your school. Think about written and unwritten rules at your school. Use this chart to list three problems and solutions that new students might face at your school. Choose the best problem and solution as the topic of your essay.

Problem			
Solution			

Listening and Speaking: Informal Discussion

Take part in an **informal discussion** about what a new student should or should not do. Answer the questions in the chart. List facts you use to back up your opinions.

	My Ideas
What could a new student do to make friends quickly?	
What should a new student not do if he or she wants to fit in?	
What can other students do to welcome new students?	

Oranges • Ode to Family Photographs

Poets use creative language for different reasons:

- to help the reader see an image

- to tell stories

- to share feelings

- to describe experiences

Poets use **sound devices** to make their writing sound musical. These devices enhance a poem's mood and meaning. This chart contains the most common sound devices.

Sound	Definition	Example
Rhyme	Repeating sounds at the ends of words	pool, rule, fool
Rhythm	Beat created by pattern of stressed and unstressed syllables	Thĕ cát săt ón thĕ mát.
Repetition	Use of any part of language (sound, word, and so on) more than one time	The tired dog watched. The tired cat slept.
Onomatopoeia	Use of words that imitate sounds	crash, bang, hiss, splat
Alliteration	Repeating consonant sounds in the beginnings of words	lovely, lonely nights

Figurative language is writing or speech that is not meant to be taken literally. The different types of figurative language are called **figures of speech**.

Poets use figurative language to express ideas or feelings in fresh ways. This chart contains the most common types of figurative language.

Figurative Language	Definition	Example
Metaphor	Describes one thing as if it were another	The snow was a white blanket over the town.
Simile	Uses *like* or *as* to compare two unlike things	She is as slow as a turtle.
Personification	Gives human qualities to something that is not human	The ocean crashed angrily during the storm.

Sensory language is writing that helps the reader use his or her senses. The five senses are sight, sound, smell, taste, and touch. Sensory language creates word pictures, or **images**. Images help the reader experience a poem.

Here are some different forms of poetry:

- **Narrative:** A narrative poem tells a story in verse. Verse is an ordered arrangement of lines. A narrative poem has a plot. It also has characters as a short story does.

- **Lyric:** Lyric poetry expresses a single speaker's thoughts and feelings. This kind of poetry often has highly musical verse.

- **Concrete:** Concrete poems are shaped to look like the subject of the poem. The poet arranges the poem's lines to create a picture on the page.

- **Haiku:** Haiku is a three-line Japanese poem in verse form. The first and third lines each have five syllables. The second line has seven syllables.

- **Limerick:** A limerick is a funny poem that has five lines. Limericks also have their own rhythm pattern and rhyme scheme.

Oranges • Ode to Family Photographs

Gary Soto

Summaries The speaker in "Oranges" is a twelve-year-old boy who shares his experience of visiting a store with a young girl. "Ode to Family Photographs" is about the photographs the poet's mother took of him and his family.

Note-taking Guide

Use this chart to record details about the characters and their actions in the poems.

	Characters	Actions
Orange	the speaker a girl a saleslady	
Ode to Family Photographs		

Which experience from your childhood would you like to write about? Briefly describe it.

_____

_____

Poetry

Sensory language creates word pictures of sight, sound, smell, taste, and touch. Read the first underlined sentence. For which two senses does the poet create word pictures? Circle the details that support your answer.

_____

_____

Vocabulary and Pronunciation

The word *breathing* in the underlined passage can have several meanings. It could mean that the boy and girl are *inhaling and exhaling air* in front of the drugstore. It could also mean that the boy and girl are *pausing to rest* in front of the drugstore. Another idea would be that the poet is trying to show that the boy and girl have arrived at the drugstore. Write a sentence using the word *breathing* in one of the ways listed above.

_____

_____

Oranges
Gary Soto

The first time I walked
With a girl, I was twelve,
Cold, and weighted down
With two oranges in my jacket.
5   December. Frost cracking
Beneath my steps, my breath
Before me, then gone,
As I walked toward
Her house, the one whose
10   Porch light burned yellow
Night and day, in any weather.
A dog barked at me, until
She came out pulling
At her gloves, face bright
15   With rouge. I smiled,
Touched her shoulder, and led
Her down the street, across
A used car lot and a line
Of newly planted trees,
20   Until we were breathing
Before a drugstore. We
Entered, the tiny bell
Bringing a saleslady
Down a narrow aisle of goods.
25   I turned to the candies
Tiered like bleachers,
And asked what she wanted
Light in her eyes, a smile
Starting at the corners
30   Of her mouth. I fingered
A nickel in my pocket,
And when she lifted a chocolate
That cost a dime,

Vocabulary Development

rouge (roozh) *n.*   red makeup for coloring cheeks
tiered (tEErd) *v.*   layered

I didn't say anything.
35 I took the nickel from
My pocket, then an orange,
And set them quietly on
The counter. When I looked up,
The lady's eyes met mine,
40 And held them, knowing
Very well what it was all
About.
          Outside,
A few cars hissing past,
45 Fog hanging like old
Coats between the trees.
I took my girl's hand
In mine for two blocks,
Then released it to let
50 Her unwrap the chocolate.
I peeled my orange
That was so bright against
The gray of December
That, from some distance,
55 Someone might have thought
I was making a fire in my hands.

© Pearson Education, Inc., publishing as Pearson Prentice Hall.

TAKE NOTES

Poetry

Narrative poetry tells a story in verse. Read the bracketed passage. What happens in this part of the poem?

_____

_____

Build English Skills

In English, you only capitalize the first letter in the first word of a sentence or a proper noun. Proper nouns are the name of a specific person, place, thing, or idea. A poet will sometimes capitalize the first letter of the first word on each line. Soto does this in "Oranges." Rewrite the underlined sentence using the correct capitalization.

_____

_____

Stop to Reflect

Why do you think the lady at the store let the boy buy the chocolate with a nickel and an orange?

_____

_____

Reading Check

What does the poet say it seems is in the boy's hands? Underline the answer.

Ode to Family Photographs
Gary Soto

Lyric poetry is normally musical. Is this poem musical? Explain.

_____

_____

_____

Soto says that there is a picture of him "with my head cut off" in the bracketed passage. This does not mean that his head has been actually cut off. This type of phrase is called a figure of speech. Given the context of the poem, what does the author probably mean?

_____

_____

Reading poetry is different from reading other types of writing. A line in poetry that ends with a period may not have a complete subject and verb. Underline an example of this between lines 15 and 20.

Was the speaker's mother good at taking pictures? Circle the text that tells you.

This is the pond, and these are my feet.
This is the rooster, and this is more of
   my feet.

Mamá was never good at pictures.

This is a statue of a famous general who
   lost an arm
5 And this is me with my head cut off.

This is a trash can chained to a gate,
This is my father with his eyes half-closed.

This is a photograph of my sister
And a giraffe looking over her
   shoulder.

10 This is our car's front bumper.
This is a bird with a pretzel in its
   beak.
This is my brother Pedro standing
   on one leg on a rock,
With a smear of chocolate on his
   face.

Mamá sneezed when she looked
15 *Behind the camera: the snapshots*
   are blurry,
The angles dizzy as a spin on a
   merry-go-round.

But we had fun when Mamá picked
   up the camera.
How can I tell?
Each of us laughing hard.
20 Can you see? I have candy in my
   mouth.

Poetry

1. **Speculate:** The saleslady in "Oranges" knows that the boy does not have enough money for the piece of chocolate. How would the girl react if she knew that the boy was poor?

_____

2. **Draw Conclusions:** How do you think the speaker feels about his mother in "Ode to Family Photographs"?

_____

3. **Poetry:** Analyze the **sensory language** in the poems by completing the chart. Write an image that uses sensory language in the first column. Then, explain what the language means in the second column. Finally, explain why the image is important to the poem in the third column.

4. **Poetry:** What do the two poems have in common?

_____

What It Says	What It Means	Why It Is Important

RESEARCH THE AUTHOR

Poster

Design a **poster** about three poems by Gary Soto. Use the following prompts to take notes for your poster.

- Search the Internet for information about Gary Soto by using word searches with the following words: "Gary Soto" and "Gary Soto poetry." Read what fans have to say about his poetry and why they like it.

  What I learned:

  _____

  _____

  _____

- Gary Soto has written ten collections of poetry. One of his books of poetry is called *Neighborhood Odes*. Read his poems to learn how he describes living in a Chicano neighborhood and his life as a young boy.

  What I learned:

  _____

  _____

  _____

- Watch the video interview with Gary Soto. Review your source material. Use this information to answer the following questions.

1. How does the poet use the world around him to write poetry?

   _____

   _____

2. How has the poet's work changed or developed over the years?

   _____

   _____

   _____

Poetry Collection 1 • Poetry Collection 2

READING SKILL

Context clues can help you guess the meaning of a word you do not know. The clues are found on the page near the new word. Context clues may have the same meaning as the new word, describe the new word, or explain the new word.

Ask questions such as these to use context clues:

- *What kind of word is it?*

- *What word can I use in place of the new word?*

- *Does the new sentence make sense?*

The chart helps you find the meaning of *stride* in this sentence:

Example: He lengthened his *stride* to catch up with his friend.

Use this chart to find the meaning of a new word from one of the poems.

LITERARY ANALYSIS

Rhythm and **rhyme** add a musical quality to poems.

- **Rhythm** is the sound pattern, or beat, created by stressed and unstressed syllables.
  Example: JACK and JILL went UP the HILL (4 stressed/3 unstressed)

- **Rhyme** is the same sound at the end of two or more words.
  Example: *delight* and *excite*

A poet sometimes sets up a rhyme pattern, also called a *scheme*. You start expecting rhymes when you see a pattern.

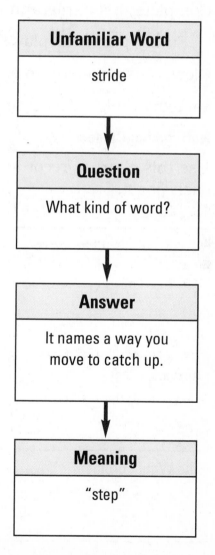

Unfamiliar Word

stride

Question

What kind of word?

Answer

It names a way you move to catch up.

Meaning

"step"

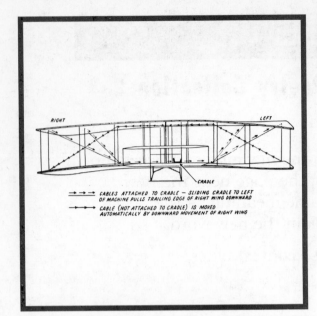

CABLES ATTACHED TO CRADLE – SLIDING CRADLE TO LEFT
OF MACHINE PULLS TRAILING EDGE OF RIGHT WING DOWNWARD

CABLE (NOT ATTACHED TO CRADLE) IS MOVED
AUTOMATICALLY BY DOWNWARD MOVEMENT OF RIGHT WING

Poetry Collection 1

Summaries Brave Isabel defeats a bear, a witch, a giant, and a doctor in "Adventures of Isabel." "Ankylosaurus" describes a tough dinosaur. How the Wright brothers built the first airplane is described in "Wilbur and Orville Wright."

Reading/Writing Connection

Complete this paragraph to describe what makes people funny.

Funny people <u>display</u> their _____ in different ways.

Clowns use makeup to <u>emphasize</u> _____. A stand-up

comedian might <u>focus</u> on _____.

Note-taking Guide

Use this chart to record information about characters' actions in each poem.

Characters	Actions
Isabel	eats a bear turns a witch into milk
Ankylosaurus	
The Wright brothers	

Adventures of Isabel
Ogden Nash

Isabel met an enormous bear,
Isabel, Isabel, didn't care;
The bear was hungry, the bear was
    ravenous,
The bear's big mouth was cruel and
    cavernous.
5 The bear said, Isabel, glad to meet you,
How do, Isabel, now I'll eat you!
Isabel, Isabel, didn't worry,
Isabel didn't scream or scurry.
She washed her hands and she
    straightened her hair up,
10 Then Isabel quietly ate the bear up.

Once in a night as black as pitch
Isabel met a wicked old witch.
The witch's face was cross and wrinkled,
The witch's gums with teeth were
    sprinkled.
15 Ho ho, Isabel! the old witch crowed,
I'll turn you into an ugly toad!
Isabel, Isabel, didn't worry,
Isabel didn't scream or scurry,
She showed no rage and she showed
    no rancor,
20 But she turned the witch into milk and
    drank her.

Isabel met a hideous giant,
Isabel continued self-reliant.
The giant was hairy, the giant was horrid,
He had one eye in the middle of his
    forehead.

Vocabulary Development

ravenous (RAV uh nuhs) *adj.*   greedily hungry
rancor (RANG ker) *n.*   bitter hate or ill will

TAKE NOTES

Activate Prior Knowledge

What characters do you remember from other poems or nursery rhymes? Write their names here.

_____

_____

Build English Skills

A contraction is the shortened form of two words. An apostrophe takes the place of one or two letters that are left out. For example, *I'm* is the contraction for *I am*. Circle the contractions in the bracketed passage. Write the two words that the contraction replaces.

_____

_____

Literary Analysis

Rhyme is the repetition of sounds at the ends of words. Rhyming can involve more than a single word. What two-word rhymes are used in lines 9 and 10?

_____

_____

Reading Check

What did the bear say to Isabel? Underline the text that tells you.

The word *zwieback* in the under-lined passage means "sweetened bread that is toasted." Circle the words in the passage that give clues to the meaning of the word.

What **context clues** help you understand that a *satchel* is something that holds things? Circle words that help you guess the meaning of *satchel*.

Do you find the description of Ankylosaurus funny or scary? Why?

_____

_____

_____

Why would Ankylosaurus make a bad dinner for another dinosaur? Underline the text that tells you.

25 Good morning Isabel, the giant said,
I'll grind your bones to make my bread.
Isabel, Isabel, didn't worry,
Isabel didn't scream or scurry.
<u>She nibbled the zwieback that she always</u>
    <u>fed off,</u>
30 And when it was gone, she cut the giant's
    head off.

Isabel met a troublesome doctor,
He punched and he poked till he really
    shocked her.
The doctor's talk was of coughs and chills
And the doctor's satchel bulged with pills.
35 The doctor said unto Isabel,
Swallow this, it will make you well.
Isabel, Isabel, didn't worry,
Isabel didn't scream or scurry.
She took those pills from the pill concocter,
40 And Isabel calmly cured the doctor.

Ankylosaurus

Jack Prelutsky

Clankity Clankity Clankity Clank!
Ankylosaurus was built like a tank,
its hide was a fortress as sturdy as steel,
it tended to be an <u>inedible</u> meal.

5 It was armored in front, it was armored
    behind,
there wasn't a thing on its minuscule mind,
it waddled about on its four stubby legs,
nibbling on plants with a mouthful of pegs.

Ankylosaurus was best left alone,
10 its tail was a cudgel of gristle and bone,
Clankity Clankity Clankity Clank!
Ankylosaurus was built like a tank.

Vocabulary Development

inedible (in ED uh buhl) *adj.*   not fit to be eaten

Wilbur Wright and Orville Wright
Rosemary and Stephen Vincent Benét

Said Orville Wright to Wilbur Wright,
"These birds are very trying.
I'm sick of hearing them cheep-cheep
About the fun of flying.
5 A bird has feathers, it is true.
That much I freely grant.
But, must that stop us, W?"
Said Wilbur Wright, "It shan't."

And so they built a glider, first,
10 And then they built another.
—There never were two brothers more
Devoted to each other.
They ran a dusty little shop
For bicycle-repairing,
15 And bought each other soda-pop
and praised each other's daring.

They glided here, they glided there,
They sometimes skinned their noses.
—For learning how to rule the air
20 Was not a bed of roses—
But each would murmur, afterward,
While patching up his bro,
"Are we discouraged, W?"
"Of course we are not, O!"

25 And finally, at Kitty Hawk
In Nineteen-Three (let's cheer it!)
The first real airplane really flew
With Orville there to steer it!
—And kingdoms may forget their kings
30 And dogs forget their bites,
But, not till Man forgets his wings,
Will men forget the Wrights.

TAKE NOTES

Read Fluently

The suffix *-ing* can be added to words to create verbs, nouns, and even adjectives. Circle the *-ing* words in the bracketed stanza. Then, label each a verb, noun, or adjective.

Literary Analysis

Underline two words that **rhyme** with *another.*

Reading Skill

Think about who is speaking in the underlined lines. What longer words do *W* and *O* stand for?

_____

_____

Culture Note

Ohio and North Carolina both take credit for the Wright brothers' first flight. Ohio claims that credit since the brothers planned and built their planes at their bike shop in the city of Dayton. North Carolina thinks that it deserves credit since the brothers actually first flew in a town called Kitty Hawk. Which state do you think deserves credit?

_____

_____

Poetry Collection 1

1. **Assess:** Is Isabel someone you would want to have as a friend? Explain.

_____

_____

2. **Evaluate:** The Wright brothers are famous throughout the world. Do you think the Wright brothers earned their fame? Why or why not?

_____

_____

3. **Reading Skill: A context clue** is a word that helps you figure out the meaning of a word you do not know. Read the following line of poetry: *nibbling on plants with a mouthful of* pegs.

   What words in the line of poetry help you answer the question "What are pegs used for?"

_____

4. **Literary Analysis:** Each poet uses **rhyming** words. Complete this chart to give examples of rhyming words. Two examples are given.

Poem	Rhyming Words		
Ankylosaurus	clank/tank		
Wilbur Wright and Orville Wright	trying/flying		
Adventures of Isabel			

SUPPORT FOR WRITING AND EXTEND YOUR LEARNING

Writing: Letter to an Author

Write a **letter to an author** of one of the poems in the collection. Answer the following questions:

- How do you feel about the poem?

_____

_____

- Why do you like or dislike the poem? Use details from the poem to support your answer.

_____

_____

Use your answers to write notes for your letter.

Research and Technology: Booklet

Make a **booklet** that contains a variety of poems and stories about dinosaurs. Complete the following tasks for each poem and story as you research:

- Describe the poem or story in one sentence.

_____

- Explain how the story or poem is like "Ankylosaurus."

_____

_____

- Explain how the story or poem is different from "Ankylosaurus."

_____

_____

Use your notes to help create your booklet.

Poetry Collection 2

Summaries "A Dream Within a Dream" describes how someone feels after having lost a love. The speaker in "Life Doesn't Frighten Me" describes all of the things she is not afraid of. A walrus and a carpenter invite some oysters on a walk in "The Walrus and the Carpenter."

Reading/Writing Connection

Complete this paragraph to describe how people form opinions about the world.

Different people <u>interpret</u> the world in _____. How

they <u>perceive</u> their surroundings will shape _____. It is

best to <u>respond</u> to other opinions with _____.

Note-taking Guide

Use this chart to record information about the characters' actions in each poem.

Characters	Actions
The speaker of "A Dream Within a Dream"	
The speaker of "Life Doesn't Frighten Me"	says boo, makes fun, smiles
The Walrus and the Carpenter	

Poetry Collection 2

1. **Respond:** Which speaker would you like to meet? Why?

_____

_____

_____

2. **Infer:** Why does the speaker of "Life Doesn't Frighten Me" smile at frightening things?

_____

_____

3. **Reading Skill: Context clues** can help you guess the meaning of a new word. Read the following line of poetry. Explain how the context clues help you understand the meaning of shoo.

I go *boo* / Make them <u>shoo</u> / I *make fun* / Way they *run*

_____

_____

4. **Literary Analysis:** Complete this chart to give examples of **rhyming** words each poet uses. Two examples are given.

Poem	Rhyming Words		
Life Doesn't Frighten Me	wall/hall/all		
A Dream Within a Dream	brow/now/avow		
The Walrus and the Carpenter			

SUPPORT FOR WRITING AND EXTEND YOUR LEARNING

Writing: Letter to an Author

Write a **letter to an author** of one of the poems in the collection. Answer the following questions:

- How do you feel about the poem?

_____

_____

- Why do you like or dislike the poem? Use details from the poem to support your answer.

_____

_____

_____

Use your answers to write notes for your letter.

Listening and Speaking: Interview

Plan an **interview** with one of the poets in this collection. Answer the following questions:

- What questions could you ask about the poem?

_____

_____

- What questions could you ask about the poet's writing habits?

_____

_____

Use your answers to develop a list of interview questions to ask the poet. Then, use the Internet or the library to find the answers to your interview questions. Your research will help you write the responses.

Instruction Manuals

ABOUT INSTRUCTION MANUALS

An **instruction manual** gives step-by-step directions for finishing a task. The text can explain the following:

- how to put something together
- how to do something
- how to use something

Most instruction manuals have these features:

- a description of something that the reader can do by following the directions
- a list of the materials the reader needs
- a series of steps explained in an order that makes sense

READING SKILL

You may come across unfamiliar words in an instruction manual. You may also find words that are used in a way you have not seen before. **Use context clues to understand specialized and technical language**. Context clues help you understand an unfamiliar word's meaning. Context clues are

- words or phrases near the unfamiliar word.
- diagrams or pictures on the same page.

See the graphic organizer for an example of how to use context clues to understand a word.

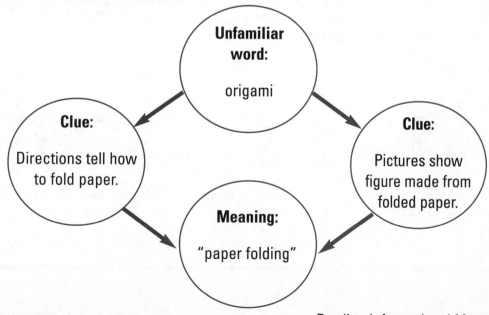

Unfamiliar word: origami

Clue: Directions tell how to fold paper.

Clue: Pictures show figure made from folded paper.

Meaning: "paper folding"

ORIGAMI

APATOSAURUS/DIMETRODON by Rachel Katz

Begin with a 9 inch by 12 inch piece of construction paper or an 8½ inch by 11 inch sheet of copy paper.

 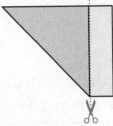  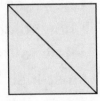

1 Place the rectangle sideways. Valley fold the left-hand side up to meet the top, thereby making a triangle.

2 Cut along the side of the triangle.

3 Save the rectangular piece of paper for the dinosaur's legs.

4 Open out the triangle into a square. Turn the square around to look like a diamond, making sure the existing fold-line is running horizontally across the paper.

Body

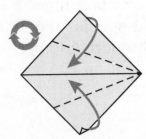 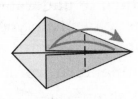 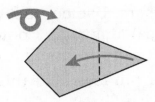

5 From the right-hand corner, valley fold the top and bottom sloping edges over to meet the middle fold-line, thereby making the kite base.

6 Valley fold the right-hand point over to meet the vertical edges. Press it flat and unfold it.

7 Turn the paper over. Valley fold the right-hand point over along the fold-line made in step 6.

8 Valley fold the point over back out toward the right.

  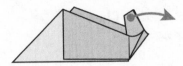

9 Valley fold the paper in half from bottom to top.

10 Reach inside the model and pull out the . . .

11 dinosaur's neck. Press it flat, into the position shown in step 12.

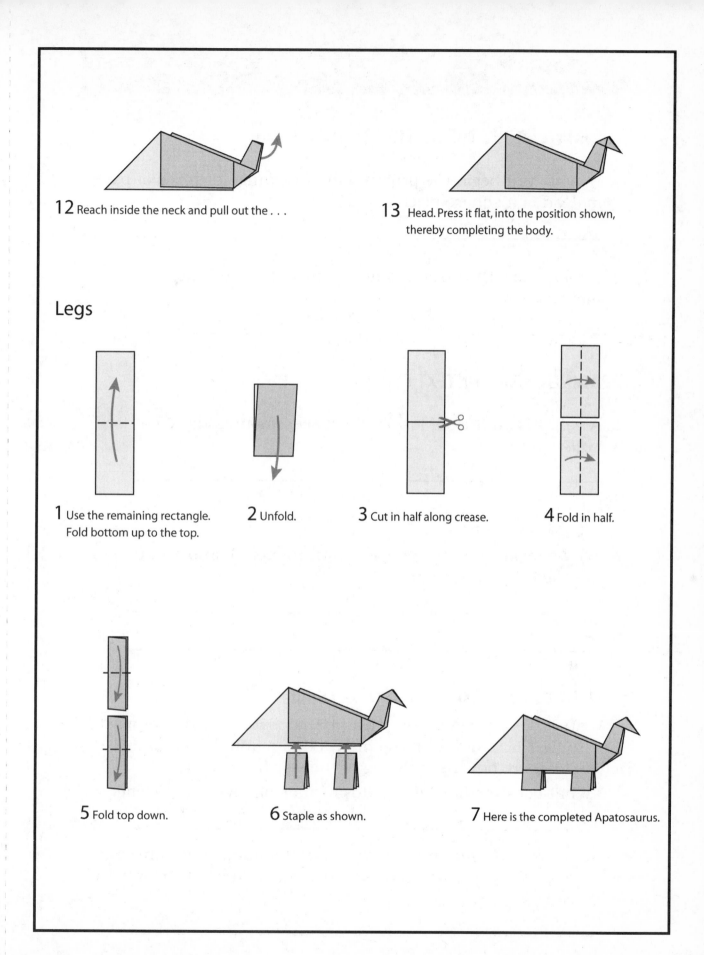

12 Reach inside the neck and pull out the . . .

13 Head. Press it flat, into the position shown, thereby completing the body.

Legs

1 Use the remaining rectangle. Fold bottom up to the top.

2 Unfold.

3 Cut in half along crease.

4 Fold in half.

5 Fold top down.

6 Staple as shown.

7 Here is the completed Apatosaurus.

THINKING ABOUT THE INSTRUCTION MANUAL

1. Why do you begin the project with a rectangular piece of paper instead of a square piece of paper?

_____

2. Explain how the diagrams help you understand the instructions.

_____

READING SKILL: CONTEXT CLUES

3. A valley is an area of low land between mountains. What is a *valley fold*?

_____

_____

4. Why do you think the shape shown in step 6 on page 202 is called a "kite base"?

_____

_____

TIMED WRITING: EXPLANATION (20 minutes)

Write a description of the origami Apatosaurus, using at least one unfamiliar word from the instruction manual. Use context clues to figure out the meaning of the word.

• What does the finished Apatosaurus look like? Be specific.

_____

• Choose a word from the instructional manual whose meaning you learned by using context clues. Explain what the word means.

_____

Poetry Collection 1 • Poetry Collection 2

READING SKILL

Context is the way a word or expression is used. Some words are hard to understand or have more than one meaning. The details around a word give you clues to the word's meaning. **Reread and read ahead** to find context clues that clarify a word's meaning. The examples below show how context makes the meaning of *hide* clear.

- **Example:** The children tried to <u>hide</u> the broken vase.
  The elephant's gray <u>hide</u> was tough and leathery.

LITERARY ANALYSIS

Figurative language is language that does not mean exactly what it says. Authors use figurative language to describe things in new ways. They may use one or more of these types of figurative language:

- **Similes** compare two unlike things using *like* or *as*. *Her eyes were as big as dinner plates.*

- **Metaphors** compare two unlike things by stating one thing is another. *Hope is an eagle.*

- **Personification** compares an object or animal to a human by giving the object or animal human qualities. *The cozy cottage hugged us on the cold night.*

See the example of figurative language in the chart. Use this chart to list examples of figurative language as you read.

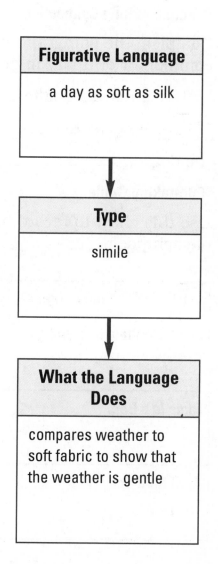

Poetry Collection 1

Summaries The speaker in "Simile: Willow and Ginko" compares the delicate willow tree and the sturdy gingko tree to show different kinds of beauty. "Fame Is a Bee" describes how fame is similar to a bee. The speaker in "April Rain Song" uses powerful images to make the rain seem alive.

Reading/Writing Connection

Complete the paragraph by explaining how to describe something common or ordinary in an uncommon way.

To compare a dog to a tornado, <u>emphasize</u> _____.

<u>Distort</u> how the dog _____. Then, <u>alter</u> a description of

the dog's _____.

Note-taking Guide

Use this chart to record important details that describe the subject of each poem.

Poem Title	Descriptions
Simile: Willow and Ginkgo	Willow: fine-lined
Fame Is a Bee	
April Rain Song	

Simile: Willow and Ginkgo
Eve Merriam

The willow is like an etching,[1]
Fine-lined against the sky.
The ginkgo is like a crude sketch,
Hardly worthy to be signed.

5 The willow's music is like a soprano,
Delicate and thin.
The ginkgo's tune is like a chorus
With everyone joining in.

The willow is sleek as a velvet-nosed calf;
10 The ginkgo is leathery as an old bull.
The willow's branches are like silken
   thread;
The ginkgo's like stubby rough wool.

The willow is like a nymph[2] with streaming
   hair;
Wherever it grows, there is green and gold
   and fair.
15 The willow dips to the water,
Protected and precious, like the king's
   favorite daughter.

The ginkgo forces its way through gray
   concrete;
Like a city child, it grows up in the street.
Thrust against the metal sky,
20 Somehow it survives and even thrives.

My eyes feast upon the willow,
But my heart goes to the ginkgo.

Vocabulary Development

chorus (KAWR us) *n.*   sound produced by many voices
   singing or speaking at the same time
thrives (thryvz) *v.*   grows well

---

1. **etching** (ECH ing) *n.* print of a drawing made on metal, glass, or wood.
2. **nymph** (nimf) *n.* spirit of nature, thought of as a beautiful maiden.

TAKE NOTES

Activate Prior Knowledge

Think about a time when you tried to explain to someone how happy or sad you felt. How did you describe how you felt?

_____

Vocabulary and Pronunciation

You can ad a *-y* to some nouns and verbs to form an adjective. "Leathery" means "like leather." Add *–y* to the following words to form adjectives.

curl _____

luck _____

Literary Analysis

Figurative language is a way writers use language to compare things. **Similes** compare two unlike things using *like* or *as*. **Metaphors** compare two unlike things by saying one thing is the other. **Personification** compares an animal or thing to a human by giving it human qualities. What two kinds of figurative language tell how the gingko grows?

_____

Reading Check

The willow and gingko are compared to types of drawings. Circle the two types of drawings described.

Dashes (—) are used to emphasize, or draw attention to, ideas. A dash can be used to show a break in thought or an interruption. Circle the dashes in "Fame Is a Bee."

Why might the poet want to show an interruption between these lines?

_____

_____

Context clues are words that help you figure out the meaning of words you do not understand. Read the bracketed passage. What does *running* mean? What context clues help you know the meaning of running?

_____

_____

Sometimes writers combine two words using a *hyphen* (-) to form new words. What word in "April Rain Song" means the same as "sleep-song"?

_____

Fame Is a Bee
Emily Dickinson

Fame is a bee.
It has a song—
It has a sting—
Ah, too, it has a wing.

April Rain Song
Langston Hughes

Let the rain kiss you.
Let the rain beat upon your head with
    silver liquid drops.
Let the rain sing you a lullaby.

5   The rain makes still pools on the sidewalk.
The rain makes running pools in the gutter.
The rain plays a little sleep-song on our
    roof at night—

And I love the rain.

Vocabulary Development

fame (faym) *n.*   the state of being known about by many people

---

Poetry Collection 1

1. **Compare and Contrast:** Merriam describes willow and gingko trees. She compares them to drawings, singers, animals, fabrics, and humans. How does she say the trees are diffferent?

   _____

   _____

2. **Interpret:** Fill out the chart below with ideas from "Fame Is a Bee." Note good and bad things about fame in the first and second columns. Reread the poem. Tell what the poem makes you think about fame in the third column.

Good Things About Fame	Bad Things About Fame	Final Response to Poem
attracts attention	attracts criticism	

3. **Reading Skill: Context clues** help you figure out the meaning of words that you do not understand. What is the meaning of *beat* in "April Rain Song"? What context clues help you figure out the meaning?

   _____

   _____

4. **Literary Analysis: Personification** gives something human qualities. Find an example of personification in one of the poems. Explain how your choice is an example of this.

   _____

SUPPORT FOR WRITING AND EXTEND YOUR LEARNING

Writing: Poem

Write a **poem** with figurative language. Use similes, metaphors, or personification to make your topic clear to your readers.

- Make a list of people and animals you have positive feelings about.

  _____

  _____

- Choose a subject from your list. _____

- What do you like about your subject? _____

  _____

- What other things share these good qualities? _____

  _____

Research and Technology: Multimedia Report

Prepare a **multimedia report** about a tree that grows in your community. Complete the chart with information about two trees in your area. Use the information to decide which tree you will use for your report.

Trees in My Community	Characteristics of Trees	Drawing of Tree Leaf
	1. 2.	
	1. 2.	

Poetry Collection 2

Summaries The speaker in "Abuelito Who" compares the fun, happy man her grandfather was with the sick, weak man he has become. "The World Is Not a Pleasant Place to Be" reminds readers of the importance of friends. "Child on Top of a Greenhouse" describes the exciting and interesting world a child sees from the roof of a greenhouse.

Reading/Writing Connection

Complete each sentence to describe how it feels to care about another person.

1. Giving <u>aid</u> to others makes people feel _____.

2. People can <u>contribute</u> their _____.

3. Some people _____ to <u>demonstrate</u> their concern.

Note-taking Guide

Use this chart to record important details that describe the people in each poem.

Poem Title	Person	Descriptions
Abuelito Who	Abuelito	dough and feathers, sad, sick, tired, hiding, blankets and spoons and big brown shoes, rain on the roof
The World Is Not a Pleasant Place to Be		
Child on Top of a Greenhouse		

Poetry Collection 2

1. **Interpret:** The speaker of "Abuelito Who" describes her grandfather as "hiding underneath the bed." Why does the speaker describe Abuelito this way?

_____

_____

2. **Interpret:** Complete the chart below with ideas from "The World Is Not a Pleasant Place to Be." Write good things about friends in the first column. Describe life without friends in the second column. Tell what the poem makes you think about friends in the third column.

Good Things About Friends	Life Without Friends	Final Response to Poem
People to play games with		

3. **Reading Skill: Context** clues help you figure out the meanings of words that you do not understand. What is the meaning of _flow_ in "The World Is Not a Pleasant Place to Be"? What context clues help you figure out the meaning?

_____

_____

4. **Literary Analysis:** A **metaphor** compares two things that are not alike by saying that one thing is the other. Find an example of a metaphor in one of the poems. Explain your choice.

_____

_____

SUPPORT FOR WRITING AND EXTEND YOUR LEARNING

Writing: Poem

Write a **poem** with figurative language. Use similes, metaphors, or personification to make your topic clear to your readers.

- Make a list of things in nature and things in your community that you have positive feelings about.

_____

_____

- Choose a subject from your list. _____

- What do you like about your subject? _____

_____

- What other things share these good qualities? _____

_____

Listening and Speaking: Poetry Reading

Prepare for a **poetry reading**. First, choose a poem to read. Then, complete this chart to help plan your reading.

Title of Poem:		
Feelings in poem:	**Words that show these feelings:**	**Voice changes and expressions that show these feelings:**
_____	_____	_____
_____	_____	_____
_____	_____	_____
_____	_____	_____

Poetry Collection 1 • Poetry Collection 2

READING SKILL

Paraphrasing is putting an author's words into your own words. Paraphrasing difficult or confusing parts in a poem helps you understand the meaning. Use these steps to paraphrase:

- Stop and **reread** any difficult lines or passages.

- Look for unfamiliar words. Find their meanings. Replace them with words that mean the same thing.

- Reread to see whether your paraphrase makes sense.

Look at the paraphrasing sample in the chart. Use the chart to help you paraphrase difficult lines as you read.

LITERARY ANALYSIS

Poets use different **forms of poetry** to go with the ideas, images, and feelings they want to express. Here are three poetic forms:

- A **concrete poem's** words are put into in a shape that looks like the subject of the poem.

- A **haiku** is a Japanese poem with three lines. Line 1 and line 3 each have five syllables. Line 2 has seven syllables.

- A **limerick** is a funny poem of five lines. Lines 1, 2, and 5 rhyme. These lines each have three beats, or stressed syllables. Lines 3 and 4 rhyme. These lines each have two beats.

Line
Afoot and lighthearted, I take to the open road.

Unfamiliar Word(s)
afoot = on foot lighthearted = happy take to = start out on

Paraphrase
On foot and happy, I start out on the road.

Poetry Collection 1

Summaries Matsuo Bashō's "Haiku" describes a quiet moment in nature. The anonymous limerick plays with words to create a fun scene. "The Sidewalk Racer" is shaped like a skateboard. The poem describes the feeling of skateboarding.

Reading/Writing Connection

Complete each sentence to describe times when people might find new ways of looking at things.

1. <u>Concentrate</u> when looking at something new to _____.

2. Some people <u>analyze</u> the clouds to _____.

3. Other people <u>display</u> their imagination when drawing _____.

Note-taking Guide

Use this chart to record what each poem is about.

Poem Title	What Poem Is About
Haiku	
Limerick	
The Sidewalk Racer	

Think about something you do often. Describe how you can look at it in a different way.

_____

_____

_____

The **haiku form of poetry** has a special number of syllables. Bashō's poem follows the syllable rule. Mark the syllables in each line.

The letters *ph* make an *f* sound in the word "asphalt." Pronounce the word "AS fawlt." Pronounce the following words giving the *ph* an *f* sound.

telephone

photograph

Use pauses when you read poetry to make the meaning more clear. Make a very short pause at the end of each line and for commas (,). Read other punctuation marks, such as periods (.), question marks, (?), and exclamation marks (!), the same way you do when reading a paragraph.

Haiku
Matsuo Bashō

An old silent pond . . .
A frog jumps into the pond,
    splash! Silence again.

Limerick
Anonymous

A flea and a fly in a flue
Were caught, so what could they do?
    Said the fly, "Let us <u>flee</u>."
    "Let us fly," said the flea.
5 So they flew through a <u>flaw</u> in the flue.

The Sidewalk Racer
or On the Skateboard
Lillian Morrison

        <u>Skimming</u>
        an asphalt sea
        I swerve, I curve, I
        sway; I speed to whirring
5   sound an inch above the
        ground; I'm the sailor
        and the sail, I'm the
        driver and the wheel
        I'm the one and only
10   single engine
        human auto
        mobile.

Vocabulary Development

flee (flee) *v.*   to run or escape from danger
flaw (flaw) *n.*   break; crack
skimming (SKIM ing) *adj.*   gliding; moving swiftly and lightly over a surface

---

Poetry Collection 1

1. **Analyze:** The limerick uses many words that begin with the sound *fl*, such as *flea*, *fly*, *flue*, and *flaw*. How does using these words make the poem funny?

_____

_____

2. **Support:** The speaker in "The Sidewalk Racer" loves skateboarding. Which words in the poem show the speaker's feeling?

_____

_____

3. **Reading Skill: Paraphrasing** is restating something in your own words. Paraphrase lines 6–12 of "The Sidewalk Racer."

_____

_____

_____

4. **Literary Analysis:** What image or word picture is presented in each line of the **haiku**? Use this web to record your answer.

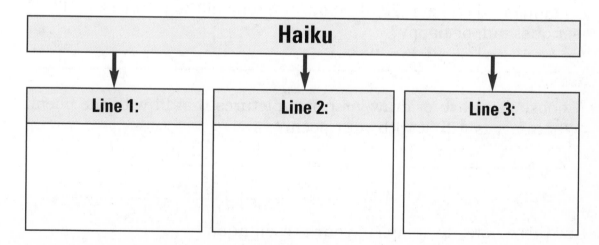

SUPPORT FOR WRITING AND EXTEND YOUR LEARNING

Support for Writing: Poem

Write your own **poem.** First, choose a topic for your poem. Then, choose the form that will work best for your topic: haiku, limerick, or concrete poem. Use the chart to help you plan ideas for your poem.

Topic of Poem:	
Form of Poem (haiku, limerick, or concrete poem):	
Style or Pattern of Form:	
Ideas for Word Choices:	

Research and Technology: Presentation of a Poem

Use a computer to design a **presentation of a poem** from this collection.

- Which poem will you design?

_____

- Choose a font, or letter style, that is easy to read. It should fit with the tone of the poem. Think about the tone of the poem. Is it silly, serious, sad, or happy?

_____

- Choose some art, or draw your own pictures that fit with the poem. What images will fit with your poem?

_____

_____

Use these notes to complete your presentation.

Poetry Collection 2

Summaries Musō Soseki's "Haiku" brings winter to life. The anonymous limerick uses rhyme and words with more than one meaning to describe an accident in a funny way. "Concrete Cat" uses nouns linked to cats. The poet lines up her words to create an image of a cat.

Reading/Writing Connection

Complete each sentence to describe poetry to someone who has never experienced it before.

1. A poet's unusual word choices can <u>motivate</u> people to

   _____.

2. Poets use words to <u>illustrate</u> _____.

3. A poem can make someone <u>modify</u> the way _____.

Note-taking Guide

Use this chart to record what each poem is about.

Poem Title	What Poem Is About
Haiku	
Limerick	
Concrete Cat	

Poetry Collection 2

1. **Infer:** The haiku describes winter winds howling through a forest. Why are there no leaves for the wind to blow in the haiku?

   _____

   _____

2. **Analyze:** _Spring_ and _fall_ have double meanings in the limerick. _Spring_ can mean a place to get water or a season. _Fall_ can mean to drop down or a season. How do these different meanings make the limerick funny?

   _____

   _____

3. **Reading Skill:** To **paraphrase** is to restate something in your own words. Review "Concrete Cat." Paraphrase the meaning of the words that form the cat's head.

   _____

   _____

4. **Literary Analysis:** What image or word picture is presented in each line of the **haiku**? Use this web to record your answer.

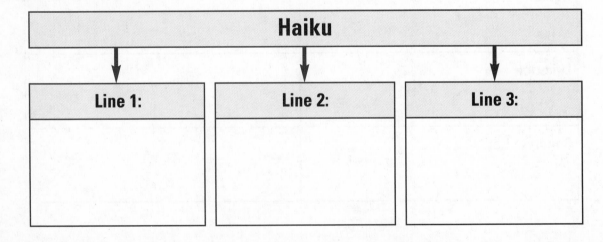

SUPPORT FOR WRITING AND EXTEND YOUR LEARNING

Support for Writing: Poem

Write your own **poem**. First, choose a topic for your poem. Then, choose the form that will work best for your topic: haiku, limerick, or concrete poem. Use the chart to help you plan ideas for your poem.

Topic of Poem:	
Form of Poem (haiku, limerick, or concrete poem):	
Style or Pattern of Form:	
Ideas for Word Choices:	

Listening and Speaking: Oral Response

Give an **oral response** to one of the poems in this collection. First, read the poem to your classmates. Then, give your opinion of the poem.

Title of Poem:	
Form of Poem (haiku, limerick, or concrete poem):	
Poem's Meaning:	
Best Words or Images from Poem:	

Use your notes to prepare your response. Remember to practice reading the poem aloud before giving your presentation.

Poetry Collection 1 • Poetry Collection 2

READING SKILL

Paraphrasing is to repeat something in your own words. Read the poem several times. Make sure that you understand the poem before you paraphrase it. Use simple words to restate the poem's meaning.

Reading aloud fluently according to punctuation will help you better understand a poem. Stop at the end of a line only if there is punctuation. Use this chart to decide where to pause.

Poetry Reading Guide	
Punctuation	**How to Read**
no punctuation	Do not pause. Keep reading.
comma (,)	slight pause
colon (:) semicolon (;) dash (—)	longer pause
period (.) question mark (?) exclamation point (!)	longest pause

LITERARY ANALYSIS

Writers use **sound devices** to bring out the music in words. Sound devices can also help a poet express feelings. Common sound devices are listed below.

- **Repetition:** the repeated use of a sound, word, or phrase. An example is *of the people, by the people, and for the people.*

- **Alliteration:** the repetition of consonant sounds at the beginning of words. An example is the *b* sound in *big bad wolf.*

- **Onomatopoeia:** the use of a word that sounds like what it means. Examples are *roar* and *buzz.*

Poetry Collection 1

Summaries "No Thank You" is a long list of reasons why the speaker does not want a kitten. "Wind and water and stone" describes how these three elements interact with one another. The playful language in "Parade" shows the excitement of a circus parade coming to town.

Reading/Writing Connection

Complete these sentences to describe why a poet might choose a common topic.

1. A poet might want readers to <u>adjust</u> the way _____.

2. A poet might want to <u>communicate</u> _____.

3. Two poets might <u>interpret</u> the same topic in _____.

Note-taking Guide

Use this chart to record important images from each poem.

Poem Title	Images
No Thank You	long hair in cornflakes sofas chewed to shreds
Wind and water and stone	
Parade	

Activate Prior Knowledge

Think about your favorite song or poem. Why do you like it?

_____

_____

_____

Build English Skills

Sometimes authors replace letters at the begin-ning or ends of words with apostrophes ('). One example is "spittin'" for "spitting." Circle two more examples in the poem.

_____

_____

Reading Skill

Reading aloud fluently accord-ing to punctuation can help you find clues to the poem's mean-ing. What should you do when you come to the ellipsis points (. . .) in the last line?

_____

_____

Reading Check

What is one thing the speaker does not like about cats? Circle a line that tells you.

No Thank You
Shel Silverstein

No I do not want a kitten,
No cute, cuddly kitty-poo,
No more long hair in my cornflakes,
No more midnight meowing mews.

5 No more scratchin', snarlin', spitters,
No more sofas clawed to shreds,
No more smell of kitty litter,
No more mousies in my bed.

No I will not take that kitten—
10 I've had lice and I've had fleas,
I've been scratched and sprayed and bitten,
I've developed allergies.

If you've got an ape, I'll take him,
If you have a lion, that's fine,
15 If you brought some walking bacon,
Leave him here, I'll treat him kind.

I have room for mice and gerbils,
I have beds for boars and bats,
But please, *please* take away that kitten—
20 Quick—'fore it becomes a cat.
Well . . . it is kind of cute at that.

Wind and water and stone
Octavio Paz

The water hollowed the stone,
the wind dispersed the water,
the stone stopped the wind.
Water and wind and stone.

5 The wind sculpted the stone,
the stone is a cup of water,
the water runs off and is wind.
Stone and wind and water.

The wind sings in its turnings,
10 the water murmurs as it goes,
the motionless stone is quiet.
Wind and water and stone.

One is the other, and is neither:
among their empty names
15 they pass and disappear,
water and stone and wind.

© Pearson Education, Inc., publishing as Pearson Prentice Hall.

Vocabulary Development

dispersed (di SPERST) *v.*   distributed in many directions

murmurs (MER merz) *v.*   makes a soft, continuous sound

TAKE NOTES

Literary Analysis

Poets use **sound devices** to bring out the music in the words. The words in the title of "Wind and water and stone" appear again and again throughout the poem. What **sound device** is the poet using?

_____

Vocabulary and Pronunciation

Sometimes the letters –*tion* are pronounced "shuhn." "Motionless" in line 11 is pronounced "MOH shuhn les." Pronounce the following words that have "shuhn" sounds.

promotion   invention

Stop to Reflect

The poet compares wind, water, and stone throughout the poem. Circle one of these examples. What is another way that you could compare wind, water, and stone?

_____

_____

Reading Check

What familiar thing that you use every day is used to describe the stone? Circle the line that tells you.

Parade

Rachel Field

Americans still have parades. They usually celebrate holidays or sporting events. What holidays or events are celebrated with parades in your native country?

_____

_____

Alliteration is the repeating of consonant sounds at the beginning of words. Circle one line in the poem that uses **alliteration**.

Bracket the sentence that describes the cage and van. The poet has changed the order the words would appear in a normal sentence. Rewrite the sentence using the sentence starter:

Each gilded cage and van will

_____

What are the floats shaped like? Underline the text that tells you.

Background

"Parade" describes an old tradition—the circus parade. Before television and radio, the best way to advertise coming attractions was a march down Main Street featuring clowns, wild animals in cages, and a giant musical instrument called a calliope.

This is the day the circus comes
With blare of brass, with beating drums,
And clashing cymbals, and with roar
Of wild beasts never heard before
5 Within town limits. Spick and span
Will shine each gilded cage and van;
Cockades at every horse's head
Will nod, and riders dressed in red
Or blue trot by. There will be floats
10 In shapes like dragons, thrones and boats,
And clowns on stilts; freaks big and small,
Till leisurely and last of all
Camels and elephants will pass
Beneath our elms, along our grass.

Vocabulary Development

leisurely (LEE zher lee) *adv.*   in an unhurried way

Poetry Collection 1

1. **Speculate:** Why do you think the speaker of "No Thank You" says that he would prefer an ape, lion, pig, or boar to a cat?

_____

_____

2. **Infer:** "Parade" contains several details about the town. What do these details suggest about the town?

_____

_____

3. **Reading Skill:** To **paraphrase** means to put something in your own words. Paraphrase the poem "No Thank You."

_____

_____

4. **Literary Analysis:** Writers use **sound devices** to express feelings and bring out the music of the words. Complete this chart by listing examples of sound devices in each poem.

	Wind and water and stone	Parade	No Thank You
Repetition		will shine, will nod, will be, will pass	
Alliteration	sculpted the stone		
Onomatopoeia			meowing

SUPPORT FOR WRITING AND EXTEND YOUR LEARNING

Writing: Prose Description

Write a **prose description** of the scene suggested by one of the poems in this collection. In other words, write a description in your own words, using regular sentences. First, choose the poem you will write about. Then, answer the following questions:

• What details from the poem do you plan to include?

_____

_____

• What details do you plan to leave out? Explain why.

_____

_____

• How would the scene in the poem make you feel if you were there?

_____

Research and Technology: Résumé

Prepare a **résumé** for one of the poets in this collection. Answer the following questions as you look for information about the poet's life:

• Where did the poet grow up? _____

_____

• Did the poet go to college? Where? _____

_____

• What other jobs has the poet had? _____

_____

• What are some of the poet's major accomplishments? _____

_____

Poetry Collection 2

Summaries Fairies warn snakes and other creatures to stay away from the sleeping Queen in "The Fairies' Lullaby." "Saying Yes" is about the speaker's struggle to express herself as a Chinese American. The speaker of "Cynthia in the Snow" enjoys the sight and sound of falling snow.

Reading/Writing Connection

Complete this paragraph to describe how art can teach you about life.

Good writers <u>capture</u> _____ in their stories and

poetry. Sometimes, their works <u>confirm</u> _____

about life. At other times, the writing will <u>contrast</u> with

_____.

Note-taking Guide

Use the chart to record important details about the three poems.

Who are the fairies protecting in "The Fairies' Lullaby"?	The fairies are protecting the fairy Queen.
What creatures do the fairies warn?	
Where is the speaker of "Saying Yes" from?	
Why does the speaker of "Cynthia in the Snow" like snow?	

Poetry Collection 2

1. **Evaluate:** Do you think that the speaker in "Saying Yes" feels good about herself? Why or why not?

_____

_____

_____

2. **Analyze:** The speaker of "Cynthia in the Snow" has an overall reaction to the snow. Describe the speaker's reaction.

_____

_____

3. **Reading Skill:** To **paraphrase** means to put something in your own words. Paraphrase the chorus's lines from "The Fairies' Lullaby."

_____

_____

_____

4. **Literary Analysis:** Writers use **sound devices** to express feelings and bring out the music of the words. Complete this chart by listing examples of sound devices in each poem.

	The Fairies' Lullaby	Cynthia in the Snow	Saying Yes
Repetition		none appears	
Alliteration			
Onomatopoeia	lullaby		none appears

SUPPORT FOR WRITING AND EXTEND YOUR LEARNING

Writing: Prose Description

Write a **prose description** of the scene suggested by one of the poems in this collection. In other words, write a description in your own words, using regular sentences. First, choose the poem you will write about. Then, answer the following questions:

- What details from the poem do you plan to include?

  _____

  _____

- What details do you plan to leave out? Explain why.

  _____

  _____

- How would the scene in the poem make you feel if you were there?

  _____

  _____

Use your notes to write your description.

Listening and Speaking: Dramatic Reading

Present a **dramatic reading** of one of the poems in this collection. Use the chart to help you prepare to read the first lines of the poem.

Poem:	How does the speaker feel?	What does the punctuation tell me to do?	Which words seem most important?
Line 1			
Line 2			
Line 3			
Line 4			

Applications

ABOUT APPLICATIONS

An **application** is a form. You use an application to give information about yourself to a person or group. Here are some reasons that people fill out applications:

- to get a library card
- to get a job
- to get into a school
- to open a bank account
- to join a club
- to get a driver's license

Read each part of an application carefully. Note any special dates or instructions.

READING SKILL

You are **reading to perform a task** when you fill out an application. The task is to give correct information. Always preview and review an application.

- **Preview:** First, look over the directions and questions. **Paraphrase**, or restate, the directions. Answer the questions listed below.

Previewing an Application
1. What information is being asked for?
2. On which line should the information be placed?
3. Must the information be typed, printed, or keyed?
4. What other documents or items should be included?
5. Which information is optional, and which is required?
6. When is the application due? To whom should it be sent?

- **Review:** Go back over the application after you have completed it. Make sure that you have filled in all of the sections. Make sure that the information is readable.

Madison County Public Library Card Application Form

The library requires I.D. and written proof of current address. All library transactions and information are strictly confidential.

Please print:

Today's Date _____ **Staff Use** Card # _____

Mr. _____ Mrs. _____ Miss _____ Ms. _____ Dr. _____

Name _____
           Last   First   Middle

Current Address _____
         Street (including house number) or PO box

City _____ State _____ Zip Code _____

Date of Birth _____

Home Telephone _____ Work Telephone _____

Patron Type—Circle One

A—Adult (age 18 & over)   YA—Young Adult (age 14–17)

J—Juvenile (age 0–13)   CS—College Student (any age)

Permanent Address (if different from current address):

_____
Street (including house number) or PO box

City _____ State _____ Zip Code _____

Parent/Legal Guardian's Name (if under age 14) _____

Driver's License or Social Security Number _____

E-mail Address (optional)_____

    I understand that by signing this form and accepting this library card I am responsible for all materials checked out using this card and for charges that may be assessed to me. I agree to give prompt notice to the library of any address change.

    If I am signing as a parent or legal guardian, I accept responsibility for my child's use of the card and agree to pay any fines or other charges incurred by my child. As a parent, I am aware that the library permits children to have access to all materials and is not responsible for restricting or censoring the materials which children may select.

Cardholder Signature _____

Parent / Legal Guardian Signature _____

STUDENT POETRY CONTEST
North Carolina Poetry Society
Deadline for Receipt of Entries: January 8, 2004
Prizes to Be Awarded
All winning poems will also be published!
- **First Place: Trophy + Certificate + $25.00**
- **Second Place: Certificate + $15.00**
- **Third Place: Certificate + $10.00**
- **Honorable Mention: Certificate**

For Students of North Carolina Schools

Who may enter this contest?
Students in grades 3–12 and college undergraduates.

What are the types of entries and awards?
- The Travis Tuck Jordan Award is for students in grades 3–5.
- The Frances W. Phillips Award is for poems about the environment and is for students in grades 3–8.
- The Mary Chilton Award is for students in grades 6–8.
- The Marie Barringer Rogers Award is for students in grades 9–undergraduate.
- The Lyman Haiku Award is for students in grades 9–undergraduate.

Note: All poems except the Lyman Haiku entries may be in any form but must have no more than 32 lines per poem.

What are the rules and how do I enter the contest?
1. You may submit one poem for each category.
2. Send two typed copies of each poem on 8½ X 11 paper.
3. In the upper left corner of each copy, type the name of the award category you are entering. Do not put your name or address on these copies.
4. On a separate piece of paper, type or print
   - the name of the category and the title of the poem you are entering
   - your name, your home address and zip code, and your phone number
   - the name of your school, your grade, your school address & telephone number, and the name of your teacher
5. Your teacher must sign the paper (see item 4 above).
6. You must also sign the paper and write: I pledge that this is my original poem.

Note: The copies of your poems that you submit to this contest will not be returned to you, so please be sure to keep copies of your poems for yourself.

THINKING ABOUT THE APPLICATION

1. Paraphrase the responsibilities a library cardholder accepts.

   _____

   _____

2. Why does the poetry contest require entrants to sign a pledge stating that their poems are original?

   _____

READING SKILL

3. What is required in order to complete the library application?

   _____

4. Which group is not eligible to enter the poetry contest?

   _____

TIMED WRITING: EXPLANATION (15 minutes)

Paraphrase the information on the library card application. Answer the following questions to help you write your explanation.

- A privilege is a benefit or advantage. What can someone do with a library card?

   _____

- Having responsibilities means that you are trustworthy or reliable. Reread the library card application. What are the responsibilities that come with having a library card?

   _____

Rewrite your answers in your own words. Then, use your notes to write your explanation.

WORDS WITH PREFIXES AND SUFFIXES

Prefixes are word parts added to the beginning of base words.

Suffixes are word parts added to the ends of words.

Master the Basics The following information will help you spell many words with prefixes and suffixes correctly.

- The spelling of a base word does not change when a prefix is added.
- To add a suffix beginning with a consonant (-*ful*, -*tion*, -*ly*):
  - Change *y* to *i* in the base word, unless a vowel comes before the *y*.
    (*pity* + *ful* = *pitiful*, but *play* + *ful* = *playful*)
  - Most other times, do not change the base word.
- To add suffixes beginning with a vowel (-*ion*, *al*, -*able*):
  - Change *y* to *i* in the base word, unless a consonant comes before the *y*. (*bury* + *al* = *burial*)
  - Usually, drop the final e in the base word. (*move* + *able* = *movable*)
  - Most other times, do not change the base word.
    (*react* + *ion* = *reaction*)

Word List
pitiful
playful
movable
reaction
misspell
irritation
burial

Practice Read the following paragraph. Circle any word that is misspelled. Then, write the misspelled word correctly on the lines below.

Grandpa saw the buryal of a time capsule under City Hall. He and his friend had a fight about the mispelling of a name. Grandpa said it should be Smith. His friend said it should be Smyth. This caused a great deal of irritateion between Grandpa and his friend. Grandma said that their reacttions were pityfull.

_____

_____

Gluskabe and Old Man Winter

Drama is written to be performed. You should imagine that you are seeing and hearing the action as you read a play. Drama shares the following elements with other forms of literature:

- **Characters:** people who take part in the action

- **Conflict:** a problem between two characters or forces

- **Theme:** a message about life

Read this chart to understand the elements of drama.

Elements of Drama	Definition	Example
Acts	units of action in drama	Act 1
Scenes	smaller parts of acts	Act 1, Scene I
Dialogue	• words that characters say • no quotation marks used • character's name placed in front of character's words	**GLUSKABE:** It is very cold this winter, Grandmother.
Script	printed form of a play, or drama	the physical copy of the play *Gluskabe and Old Man Winter*
Stage directions	• written as information in brackets • describe what stage looks like • describe how characters should act	*[Dark room with one lamp glowing; Jeb looks tired.]*
Set	arrangement of scenery that shows time and place of action	wigwam in corner with bare trees, snow on the ground
Props	objects on the stage that actors use	book, suitcase, flashlight

There are three types of plays, or drama:

- **Drama** is a word often used to describe a play with a serious subject.

- **Comedy** is a type of drama that is funny or has a happy ending. Some comedies are written for entertainment. Others are written to look at serious issues in a humorous way.

- **Tragedy** is a drama that ends with the downfall of the main character. This character is usually a very important person, such as a king.

Drama is often written for stage performance. The dramatic format is also used for scripts written for other types of performances:

- **Screenplays** are scripts for movies. They include camera angles and scene changes that are not usually in a stage play.

- **Teleplays** are screenplays written for television.

- **Radio plays** are scripts written for radio broadcasts. They sometimes include sound effects. Radio plays do not have scenery description.

Gluskabe and Old Man Winter

Joseph Bruchac

Summary Old Man Winter stays too long. A human being asks Gluskabe and Grandmother Woodchuck to end winter so his people will live. Gluskabe goes to Old Man Winter after getting advice from Grandmother Woodchuck. Gluskabe has to be clever. He ends winter with the help of Grandmother Woodchuck's advice.

Note-taking Guide

Fill in this chart with details about Gluskabe.

What is Gluskabe's job?	His job is to help the people.
Why does Gluskabe go to Old Man Winter's wigwam?	
Who gives Gluskabe advice?	
How does Gluskabe trick the Summer People?	
Where does Gluskabe take the summerstick?	

Which season of the year might you want to change? Explain why.

_____

_____

_____

_____

Drama

The **set** is the scenery that shows the time and place of the action. Where does Scene I take place? Circle the answer.

Culture Note

Family names in Native American culture often show a connection to an animal or to nature. What influences the naming of a person in your native country?

_____

_____

Drama

Conflict is a problem between characters or between a character and a force, such as nature. What is the conflict at the beginning of the play?

_____

_____

Gluskabe and Old Man Winter
Joseph Bruchac

Characters

Speaking Roles:
NARRATOR
GLUSKABE
GRANDMOTHER
   WOODCHUCK
HUMAN BEING
OLD MAN WINTER

FOUR OR MORE SUMMER
   LAND PEOPLE,
   INCLUDING THE
   LEADER
FOUR CROWS

Non-speaking Roles:
SUN
FLOWERS
PLANTS

Scene I: Gluskabe and Grandmother Woodchuck's Wigwam

◆   ◆   ◆

Gluskabe and his grandmother sit together, wrapped in blankets.

◆   ◆   ◆

NARRATOR. Long ago Gluskabe (gloo-SKAH-bey) lived with his grandmother, Woodchuck, who was old and very wise. Gluskabe's job was to help the people.

◆   ◆   ◆

Gluskabe and his grandmother talk about the winter. It has been very cold for a long time. A human being who is their friend visits. They welcome their guest.

◆   ◆   ◆

HUMAN BEING. Gluskabe, I have been sent by the other human beings to ask you for help. This winter has been too long. If it does not end soon, we will all die.

GLUSKABE. I will do what I can. I will go to the wigwam of Old Man Winter. He has stayed here too long. I will ask him to go back to his home in the Winter Land to the north.

◆   ◆   ◆

Grandmother Woodchuck tells Gluskabe to be careful. He tells her not to worry. Then he leaves, and the scene ends.

◆ ◆ ◆

Scene II: The Wigwam of Old Man Winter

OLD MAN WINTER *sits in his wigwam, "warming" his hands over his fire made of ice. The four balls of summer are on one side of the stage.*

◆ ◆ ◆

Carrying a bag, Gluskabe enters and taps on Old Man Winter's wigwam. Old Man Winter tells him to come in and sit by his fire. Gluskabe tells Old Man Winter that he must go back to his home in the Winter Land because the people are suffering in the very cold weather. Old Man Winter throws a sheet of ice over Gluskabe. He then throws Gluskabe outside. The sun melts the ice, and Gluskabe decides to ask his wise grandmother what to do next.

◆ ◆ ◆

GRANDMOTHER WOODCHUCK. It is still winter, Gluskabe! Did Old Man Winter refuse to speak to you?

GLUSKABE. We spoke, but he did not listen. I will speak to him again; and I will make him listen. But tell me, Grandmother, where does the warm weather come from?

GRANDMOTHER WOODCHUCK. It is kept in the Summer Land.

◆ ◆ ◆

Gluskabe vows to go there and bring summer back with him. Grandmother Woodchuck warns him that the Summer Land people are strange and dangerous. Each of them has only one eye. They keep summer in a big pot that they dance around. Four huge crows guard the pot. The crows swoop down and bite off the head of whoever tries to steal summer. Gluskabe is not scared. He will cover one of his eyes so

TAKE NOTES

Drama

Stage directions give information about what is on the stage. They also describe the characters' actions. Read the bracketed stage directions. What element of drama are the four balls?

_____

_____

Read Fluently

Read the underlined sentence. *Carrying a bag* is a modifier that describes a noun in this sentence. Modifiers often begin with the *-ing* form of a verb. Modifiers should be placed right next to the noun that they describe. Put a box around the noun that this modifier describes.

Build English Skills

A compound verb names two or more actions done by the same subject. For example, They *dance* and *sing*. Underline two sentences in the bracketed paragraph that contain compound verbs.

The word *fools* in the underlined sentence means "tricks or to makes someone believe something that is not true." When the word *fools* is used as a noun, it means "people who lack judgment." Rewrite the underlined sentence and replace the word *fools*. Make sure the meaning on the sentence is the same.

_____

_____

Drama

What **prop** does Gluskabe take to Old Man Winter? Underline the answer. How does Gluskabe's action solve the **conflict** of the play?

_____

_____

_____

Stop to Reflect

What connection can you make between the summerstick that Gluskabe grabs and the four seasons?

_____

_____

_____

that the Summer Land people think that he is one of them. He puts the four balls into his bag as the scene ends.

◆ ◆ ◆

Scene III: The Summer Land Village

The SUMMER LAND PEOPLE *are dancing around the pot full of summer. They are singing a snake dance song, following their leader, who shakes a rattle in one hand. Four Crows stand guard around the pot as the people dance.*

◆ ◆ ◆

The people stop dancing when Gluskabe greets them. He fools them into believing that he is one of them. They invite him to join their dance. Gluskabe reaches into the pot and grabs one of the summersticks. The people shout to the crows to bite off his head. Gluskabe holds up the balls from his bag. Each crow takes a ball, thinking that it is Gluskabe's head. Then Gluskabe runs offstage with the summerstick, and the scene ends.

◆ ◆ ◆

Scene IV: The Wigwam of Old Man Winter

◆ ◆ ◆

Gluskabe takes the summerstick to the wigwam of Old Man Winter and taps on the door. Old Man Winter invites him to come in and sit by his fire. Gluskabe once again tells Old Man Winter that he must go home to the Winter Land. He points out that the summerstick is melting the icy fire and the wigwam. Old Man Winter runs offstage, crouching to show that he is melting and growing smaller. Suddenly the bright sun and summer flowers enter the scene.

◆ ◆ ◆

NARRATOR. So Gluskabe defeated Old Man Winter. Because he brought only one small piece of summer, winter still returns each year. But, thanks to Gluskabe, spring always comes back again.

Drama

1. **Infer:** Why does Gluskabe need Grandmother Woodchuck's advice before he can defeat Old Man Winter?

   _____

   _____

2. **Analyze:** Gluskabe learns what he has to do to get summersticks from the Summer Land people. What is Gluskabe's plan?

   _____

   _____

3. **Drama: Conflict** is a struggle between two characters or between a character and a force, such as nature. What is the main **conflict** in this **drama**?

   _____

   _____

4. **Drama:** The **dialogue** is what characters say in a play. List actions taken by Old Man Winter in the second column of this chart. Then, list dialogue about Old Man Winter in the third column.

Character	Actions of the Character	Dialogue About the Character
Old Man Winter		

RESEARCH THE AUTHOR

Storytelling Program

Plan a **storytelling program** that features traditional tales by Joseph Bruchac. Follow these steps:

- Search the Internet for information about Joseph Bruchac. Look for stories that he has written and performed. Use word searches with "Joseph Bruchac," "Joseph Bruchac stories," and "Joseph Bruchac perform." Bruchac has his own Web site at www.josephbruchac.com. It is important to search other sites for additional information about him.

What I learned: _____

_____

_____

- Read as many of Bruchac's Native American stories as you can. Become familiar with his characters and the ways they speak. Read a few of the stories aloud. Listen for the way that the language sounds as you read. Decide how you think the story would sound best out loud.

What I learned: _____

_____

_____

_____

- Watch the video interview with Joseph Bruchac. Review your source material. Use this information to answer the following questions.

1. Why does Joseph Bruchac like to tell stories?

_____

_____

2. How does the storyteller turn folk tales into plays?

_____

_____

The Phantom Tollbooth, Act I

READING SKILL

A **summary** is a short statement of the main ideas and events in a piece of writing. Follow these directions when you write a summary:

- **Reread to identify main events**.

- Include only major events that move the story forward.

- Organize events in the order in which they happen.

Use this chart to help you fill in the main events from Act I, Scene ii.

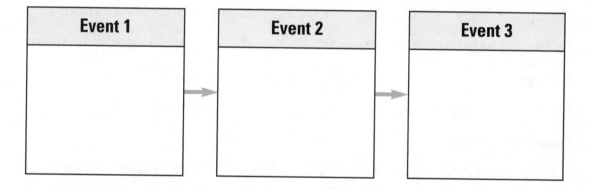

Event 1	Event 2	Event 3

LITERARY ANALYSIS

A **drama** is a story that is written to be performed. Dramas have characters, a setting, and a plot. Dramas also have these elements:

- **Dialogue:** the words the characters speak

- **Script:** the written form of the play. Characters' names appear right before what they say:

> KATRINA. I can't believe you said that!
> WALLACE. I was only kidding.

Pay attention to what characters say to help you understand the script.

The Phantom Tollbooth, Act I

Susan Nanus

Based on the book by Norton Juster

Summary A bored young boy named Milo comes home from school. He finds a wrapped gift in his room. Inside the box he finds a tollbooth. Milo sets off on an adventure into a fantasy world. Read Act I, Scene ii on the following pages.

Reading/Writing Connection

Complete these sentences to describe possible cures for boredom.

1. People who are bored need _____ to <u>motivate</u> them.

2. Many students like to <u>participate</u> in _____.

3. Some people <u>require</u> _____ to avoid boredom.

Note-taking Guide

Fill in this chart with some details about the main characters in the story. Briefly describe their behavior in the space provided.

Character	Behavior
Milo	Confused about being in strange places and talking to strange people
Tock	Encourages Milo to keep moving along
Azaz	
Mathemagician	
Spelling Bee	
Humbug	

The Phantom Tollbooth, Act I

Susan Nanus

Based on the book by Norton Juster

Cast (in order of appearance)

THE CLOCK

MILO, A BOY

THE WHETHER MAN

SIX LETHARGARIANS

TOCK, THE WATCHDOG
   (SAME AS THE CLOCK)

AZA, THE UNABRIDGED,
   KING OF DICTIONPOLIS

THE MATHEMAGICIAN,
   KING OF DIGITOPOLIS

PRINCESS SWEET RHYME

PRINCESS PURE REASON

GATEKEEPER OF
   DICTIONPOLIS

THREE WORD MERCHANTS

THE LETTERMAN (FOURTH
   WORD MERCHANT)

SPELLING BEE

THE HUMBUG

THE MINISTERS

The Sets

1. MILO'S BEDROOM—with shelves, pennants, pictures on the wall, as well as suggestions of the characters of the Land of Wisdom.

2. THE ROAD TO THE LAND OF WISDOM—a forest, from which the Whether Man and the Lethargarians emerge.

3. DICTIONOPOLIS—a market place full of open air stalls as well as little shops. Letters and signs should abound.

◆ ◆ ◆

Act 1, Scene ii The Road to Dictionopolis.

◆ ◆ ◆

(ENTER MILO in his car.)

◆ ◆ ◆

MILO. This is weird! I don't recognize any of this scenery at all. (A SIGN is held up before MILO, startling him.) Huh? (Reads.) WELCOME TO EXPECTATIONS. INFORMATION, PREDICTIONS AND ADVICE CHEERFULLY OFFERED. PARK HERE AND BLOW HORN. (MILO blows horn.)

Vocabulary Development

expectations (ek spek TAY shuhnz) *n.* feelings or beliefs about the way things should be

---

TAKE NOTES

Activate Prior Knowledge

Describe the setting of a fantasy world you have encountered in a book or a movie.

_____

_____

_____

_____

Build English Skills

The characters' names in this play fit their personality or what they do. For example, find the character's name SPELLING BEE. This character spells difficult words. Circle the character that probably is very good in mathematics.

Literary Analysis

Dialogue is the words that characters speak to one another. Circle the word that shows you which character is speaking in the first dialogue.

Reading Check

In what order is the cast listed? Circle the answer in the text.

A **script** is the written form of a **drama**, or a story that is written to be performed. What does the script tell you that Milo is doing in the bracketed passage?

_____

_____

The word *doldrums* is pronounced (DOHL druhmz) and means "sluggishness" or "inactivity." Write two words to describe how someone in the doldrums might feel.

1. _____

2. _____

The underlined sentence has three pronouns. Pronouns are words that replace nouns. Use a pronoun so that you do not have to repeat the noun over and over again. For example, the pronoun for Sarah is *she*. Circle the pronouns in the underlined sentence.

WHETHER MAN. *(A little man wearing a long coat and carrying an umbrella pops up from behind the sign. . . . He speaks very fast and excitedly.)* My, my, my, my, my, welcome, welcome, welcome, welcome to the Land of Expectations, Expectations, Expectations! . . . Now what can I do for you? I'm the Whether Man.

MILO. *(Referring to map.)* Uh . . . is this the right road to Dictionopolis?

WHETHER MAN. Well now, well now, well now, I don't know of any *wrong* road to Dictionopolis, so if this road goes to Dictionopolis at all, it must be the right road, and if it doesn't, it must be the right road to somewhere else, because there are no wrong roads to anywhere. Do you think it will rain?

MILO. I thought you were the Weather Man.

WHETHER MAN. Oh, no, I'm the Whether Man, not the weather man. . . . After all, it's more important to know whether there will be weather than what the weather will be. . . .

◆　◆　◆

The Whether Man is no help, so Milo leaves. Soon his car slows to a stop. He has entered the Doldrums, a place where nothing ever happens and nothing ever changes. <u>He meets the Lethargarians, who pass their days sleeping, daydreaming, wasting time, and never thinking.</u> Milo begins to yawn. The Lethargarians invite Milo to join them. He is just about to do so when the Watchdog arrives. Watchdog does not like it when people waste time.

◆　◆　◆

WATCHDOG. What are you doing here?

MILO. Nothing much. Just killing time. You see. . . .

WATCHDOG. KILLING TIME! *(His ALARM RINGS in fury.)* It's bad enough wasting time without killing it. What are you doing in the Doldrums anyway? Don't you have anywhere to go?

MILO. I think I was on my way to Dictionopolis when I got stuck here. Can you help me?

WATCHDOG. Help you! You've got to help yourself. I suppose you know why you got stuck.

MILO. I guess I just wasn't thinking.

WATCHDOG. Precisely. Now you're on your way.

MILO. I am?

WATCHDOG. Of course. Since you got here by not thinking, it seems reasonable that in order to get out, you must start thinking. Do you mind if I get in? I love automobile rides. *(He gets in. They wait.)* Well?

MILO. All right. I'll try. *(Screws up his face and thinks.)* Are we moving?

WATCHDOG. Not yet. Think harder.

MILO. I'm thinking as hard as I can.

WATCHDOG. Well, think just a little harder than that. Come on, you can do it.

MILO. All right, all right. . . . I'm thinking of all the planets in the solar system, and why water expands when it turns to ice, and all the words that begin with "q," and . . . *(The wheels begin to move.)* We're moving! We're moving!

◆ ◆ ◆

Milo heads to Dictionopolis with the Watchdog, whose name is Tock. On the way, Tock tells Milo about a terrible argument that had taken place between King Azaz, the king of Dictionopolis, and the Mathemagician, the king of Digitopolis. King Azaz had said that words were more important than numbers. The Mathemagician had said that numbers were more important than words.

The Princesses Rhyme and Reason had tried to settle the argument between the two rulers. They declared that words and numbers are equally important. Azaz and the Mathemagician disagreed with the Princesses' decision. So, they sent the Princesses away to the Castle-in-the-Air.

© Pearson Education, Inc., publishing as Pearson Prentice Hall.

TAKE NOTES

Reading Skill

A **summary** is a short statement of the main ideas and events of a piece of writing. Write two sentences summarizing Milo's conversation with the Watchdog.

_____

_____

_____

_____

Literary Analysis

How does Milo and the Watchdog's **dialogue** help you understand the problem here?

_____

_____

_____

_____

Reading Check

What three things does Milo think about to get himself and the Watchdog out of the Doldrums? Underline the answers.

Read the first bracketed passage in the **script**. What can be seen as the banquet begins?

_____

_____

_____

The ministers use many words to describe one thing or idea. Do you think it is better to use many words or one word to communicate an idea? Circle the words the ministers use that you would use if you were one of them.

_____

_____

_____

Summarize what happens in the second bracketed passage.

_____

_____

_____

Soon Milo and Tock arrive in Dictionopolis. They visit a market where people buy and sell "juicy tempting words." There they meet Humbug and the Spelling Bee, and the King's advisors invite them to attend the Royal Banquet. Trumpets sound, and a PAGE appears.

◆ ◆ ◆

PAGE. King Azaz the Unabridged is about to begin the Royal banquet. . . . *(A huge Table is carried out with* KING AZAZ *sitting in a large chair, carried out at the head of the table.)*

AZAZ. Places. Everyone take your places. *(All the characters . . . rush to take their places at the table.* MILO *and* TOCK *sit near the* KING. AZAZ *looks at* MILO.*)* And just who is this?

MILO. Your Highness, my name is Milo and this is Tock. Thank you very much for inviting us to your banquet, and I think your palace is beautiful!

MINISTER 1. Exquisite.

MINISTER 2. Lovely.

MINISTER 3. Handsome.

MINISTER 4. Pretty.

MINISTER 5. Charming.

AZAZ. SILENCE! Now tell me, young man, what can you do to entertain us? Sing songs? Tell stories? Juggle plates? . . .

MILO. I can't do any of those things.

AZAZ. What an ordinary little boy. Can't you do anything at all?

MILO. I can count to a thousand.

AZAZ. AARGH, numbers! Never mention numbers here . . . Now why don't we change the subject and have some dinner? Since you are the guest of honor, you may pick the menu.

◆ ◆ ◆

Vocabulary Development

unabridged (un uh BRIJD) *adj.* complete; things that are abridged, such as some dictionaries, do not contain all of the material that is in the original

Milo asks for a light snack, and trays of light are carried in. Next, he requests a square meal, and waiters serve trays of colored squares. The guests do not like either of the meals.

◆ ◆ ◆

AZAZ. *(Claps his hands and the trays are removed.)* Time for speeches. *(To MILO.)* You first.

MILO. (Hesitantly.) Your Majesty, ladies and gentlemen, I would like to take this opportunity to say that. . . .

AZAZ. That's quite enough. Mustn't talk all day.

MILO. But I just started to . . .

AZAZ. NEXT!

HUMBUG. *(Quickly.)* Roast turkey, mashed potatoes, vanilla ice cream.

SPELLING BEE. Hamburgers, corn on the cob, chocolate pudding p-u-d-d-i-n-g. *(Each Guest names two dishes and a dessert.)*

AZAZ. *(The last. . . . He claps his hands. Waiters serve each Guest his Words.)* Dig in. *(To MILO.)* Though I can't say I think much of your choice.

MILO. I didn't know I was going to have to eat my words.

AZAZ. Of course, of course, everybody here does. Your speech should have been in better taste.

MINISTER 1. Here, try some somersault. It improves the flavor.

MINISTER 2. Have a rigamarole. *(Offers bread-basket.)*

MINISTER 3. Or a ragamuffin.

MINISTER 4. Perhaps you'd care for a synonym bun.

MINISTER 5. Why not wait for your just desserts?[1] . . .

◆ ◆ ◆

Dessert is served. Afterwards, all guests leave, except Milo, Tock, and Humbug. They stay and talk with the King about a problem in Dictionopolis. Milo suggests that Azaz let Rhyme and Reason return to solve the

---

1. just desserts *n.* what a person deserves.

TAKE NOTES

Culture Note

When Milo asks for a square meal he gets actual squares. A *square meal* in America refers to a meal that is nutritionally complete, or healthful. Such a meal might have meat, vegetables, potatoes or rice, and maybe some fruit. What is considered a square meal in your native country?

_____

_____

Reading Skill

Organize events in the order in which they happen when you write a **summary**. List in order the two main things that happen on this page.

1. _____

_____

2. _____

_____

Stop to Reflect

The common expression *eat my words* means "admit I was wrong." How is this meaning different from Milo's meaning in the underlined passage?

_____

_____

_____

Reading Skill

Summarize the steps that Milo will have to take to rescue the princesses.

_____

_____

_____

_____

_____

_____

Literary Analysis

Dialogue can give you information about characters. Read the bracketed dialogue. How do you think Milo and Tock feel about the journey?

_____

_____

_____

Reading Check

What does Azaz give Milo for protection? Circle the answer.

problem. Azaz likes Milo's idea but says rescuing the princesses is too difficult. Humbug says Milo could do the job.

He says all he would have to do is travel across the dangerous unknown countryside to Digitopolis. There he would persuade the Mathemagician (who never agrees with Azaz about anything) to agree to the plan. Next he would enter the Mountains of Ignorance from which no one has ever returned alive. From there he would climb a two-thousand-foot stairway to the Castle-in-the-Air, rescue the princesses, and fight off frightening fiends as they made their way back to Dictionopolis.

◆ ◆ ◆

AZAZ. I never realized it would be so simple.

MILO. It sounds dangerous to me. . . .

AZAZ. Dictionopolis will always be grateful to you, my boy, and your dog. (_AZAZ pats TOCK and MILO._)

TOCK. Now, just one moment, sire . . .

AZAZ. You will face many dangers on your journey, but fear not, for I can give you something for your protection. (_AZAZ gives MILO a box._) In this box are the letters of the alphabet. With them you can form all the words you will ever need to help you overcome the <u>obstacles</u> that may stand in your path. . . .

◆ ◆ ◆

Azaz says Humbug will be their guide. He sends them on their way. Suddenly, the travelers hear a frightening noise up ahead. They look at each other fearfully. The lights fade.

Vocabulary Development

obstacles (AHB sti kuhlz) _n._   things that make it difficult to succeed at something

---

The Phantom Tollbooth, Act 1

1. **Identify Cause and Effect:** Dictionopolis has been having a hard time since Rhyme and Reason were banished. What effect does the absence of Rhyme and Reason have on Dictionoplis?

_____

2. **Predict:** In Act II, Milo will start his journey. What do you think his journey will be like? Give two details from Act I to support your answer.

_____

_____

3. **Reading Skill:** What three events would you include in a **summary** of Act I?

_____

_____

4. **Literary Analysis: Dialogue** helps readers know about a character's personality, the setting, and an action. Fill in this chart with information about what the dialogue shows. An example has been provided.

Dialogue	What It Suggests
MILO: Nothing much. Just killing time.	**Character:** Milo is bored. He does not care about anything.
MILO: WELCOME TO EXPECTATIONS. INFORMATION, PREDICTIONS AND ADVICE CHEERFULLY OFFERED.	**Setting:**
WATCHDOG: Do you mind if I get in? I love automobile rides.	**Action:**

SUPPORT FOR WRITING AND EXTEND YOUR LEARNING

Writing: Summary

Write a **summary** of Act I. A summary includes the most important events. Answer the following questions to help you write your summary.

• Why is Dictionopolis such an unusual place?

_____

_____

_____

_____

• Which details make the story interesting?

_____

_____

_____

• Which information from the stage directions should you include in your summary?

_____

_____

Listening and Speaking: Speech

Write a **speech** that Milo might have given at the banquet. Imagine that you are Milo. Fill in the following chart with details for your speech.

Milo's first experience in Dictionopolis	Characters he meets along the way	Milo's gratitude for being invited to the banquet

Problem-and-Solution Essays

ABOUT PROBLEM-AND-SOLUTION ESSAYS

A **problem-and-solution essay** begins by explaining a problem. This kind of essay also gives solutions to that problem. The problem can be personal, local, or universal. Problem-and-solution essays contain these features:

- a description of the problem
- a description of ways to solve the problem
- details that support important points
- clear organization

READING SKILL

An outline is a list of main ideas and important details. **Outlining** can help you do the following:

- draw attention to the most important ideas
- draw attention to the supporting details

Follow these steps to create an outline:

1. Find the main ideas in the essay.
2. List subtopics for each main idea.
3. List details that support the subtopics.

Use this example of an outline to help you take notes as you read.

I. First Main Idea
A. First subtopic
1. Supporting detail
2. Supporting detail
B. Second subtopic
1. Supporting detail
2. Supporting detail

BOREDOM BLUES BEGONE
Sherri Regalbuto

If you've ever watched a documentary on zoo animals, you will have noticed that a great deal of time is spent on making sure the zoo animals do not become bored. An animal that lives in the same surroundings and is fed in the same manner and at the same time every day can become bored and depressed. Keeping our dogs from becoming bored is just as important. Bored dogs can get into all sorts of trouble if left to entertain themselves. You can entertain, educate, and enrich the life of your canine with these simple activities:

- Take some small dry treats and hide them around the house while your dogs are in another room. <u>Make sure they are easily accessible for your dogs so they don't have to scratch anything up to get them.</u> Let your dogs out and tell them to find the treats. Help with the first couple if you need to.

- Take a big old pile of blankets and hide treats in the blankets. Set your dogs loose on the pile and tell them to "find" the treats.

- Bobbing is another fun activity, especially on a summer day that is too hot to venture out. Fill a kiddy pool, large pot or pail with a couple of inches of water. Throw your dogs' favorite waterproof toys or water-tough treats (meaty type) into the water and let them figure out how to get them out. Some dogs are naturals at this, but some can take a while to figure out how to get the toy without getting water up their noses. Don't push: Let them figure it out on their own time. Many dogs will learn how to retrieve items from underwater once they learn the "don't sniff under water" rule.

- Got a digger demolishing your backyard? Build a sandbox for your digger and hide treats (dry cracker type) under the sand. Once dogs are rewarded for digging in this area, they are sure to adopt the new digs!

- When you purchase new toys, keep some put away. Bring a new one out each week and put an old one away. Just like kids, dogs like to get a new toy and the new toy is always the favorite of the week.

- Plan a play date. Play dates are a wonderful activity for you and your dog. If you know of someone with a friendly dog, invite them over to play in your backyard. Not only will your dog have a new playmate, you will have fun discussing your dogs having so much fun.

- Mealtime can be very boring for dogs. Take their regular ration of food and stuff it into an indestructible toy and let them scavenge it out. Hide dry dog food around the house or use it for your obedience and trick training. Dogs do not have to eat their meal out of a bowl.

- Give your dog a new toy each week. You can have half a dozen toys and each week bring out a new one and put the old one back in storage—that way there is always something new for the dog to enjoy.

- Obedience and trick training is a wonderful activity. Done in a fun and positive method, your dog will love school time.

Use your imagination and introduce your dog to some new, fun, and different ways for the two of you to spend your time together.

TAKE NOTES

Reading Skill

An **outline** can help you summarize information in a text. It points out the important ideas and supporting details. What are the important ideas in this essay?

_____

_____

Reading Informational Materials

Do you think the author did a good job of describing solutions to the problem of boredom in dogs? Why or why not?

_____

_____

_____

_____

Culture Note

There are more than 60 million pet dogs in America. The 5 most popular dog breeds (according to the American Kennel Club, 2002) are Labrador Retriever, Golden Retriever, German Shepherd, Beagle, and Dachshund.

Reading Check

What should you do when you buy new toys? Circle the text that tells you.

THINKING ABOUT THE PROBLEM-AND-SOLUTION ESSAY

1. Describe ways that animals in the wild avoid becoming bored.

   _____

2. Describe surroundings that would provide activities for dogs.

   _____

READING SKILL

3. Does the detail *Mealtime can be boring for a dog* support the idea that "a busy dog is a happy dog"? Explain.

   _____

   _____

4. Does the detail *Dogs can become depressed when they are bored* support the problem presented in the essay? Explain your answer.

   _____

   _____

TIMED WRITING: SUMMARY (20 minutes)

Create an informal outline of the essay. Then, write a brief summary of the essay. Answer the following questions:

- What is the main problem in the essay?

   _____

- What main solution does the author give?

   _____

- What are two suggestions the author gives?

   _____

The Phantom Tollbooth, Act II

READING SKILL

Compare two things to tell how they are alike. **Contrast** two things to tell how they are different. **Picture the action** as you read drama. Pay attention to the dialogue and the descriptions of how characters speak and act. Picturing the action will help you compare and contrast characters, situations, and events.

LITERARY ANALYSIS

Stage directions are the words in a drama that the characters do not say. Directions give the following information:

- where performers should move
- how performers should speak
- how readers can picture the action, sounds, and scenery

Stage directions are usually printed in italics and set between brackets. See this example:

> **CARLOS.** [*To* ISABEL.] Remember, don't make a sound!
> [*He tiptoes offstage.*]

Fill in this chart to record stage directions as you read. The directions should help you picture the action. They will also help you understand what the characters are thinking and feeling.

Stage Directions
What It Shows About the Character or Action

The Phantom Tollbooth, Act II

Susan Nanus
Based on the book by Norton Juster

Summary Milo, Tock, and Humbug arrive in Digitopolis in Scene i. They ask the Doctor of Dissonance, the Dodecahedron, and the Mathemagician which road to take to find the Princesses. They arrive in the Land of Ignorance to rescue the Princesses. After they succeed, Milo learns an important lesson.

Reading/Writing Connection

Complete the following sentences to explain the importance of words and numbers.

1. The right words always help <u>clarify</u> _____.

2. It is impossible to <u>compute</u> _____ without numbers.

3. It is important to know how to <u>define</u> a word to _____.

Note-taking Guide

Milo, Tock, and Humbug meet many challenges in the Land of Ignorance. Fill in this chart with information about the challenges that the three face.

Character	Challenges to Milo, Tock, and Humbug
Everpresent Wordsnatcher	Confuses words and meanings
Terrible Trivium	
Demon of Insincerity	
Senses Taker	

The Phantom Tollbooth, Act II

Act II, Scene ii The Land of Ignorance

Rhyme and Reason are locked in the castle. Rhyme is nervous that Milo, Tock, and Humbug will not save them. Reason calms down her sister. She says that Milo has learned much on his journey.

Milo drives through the Land of Ignorance. Tock and Humbug are with him. They meet a well-dressed man. The man welcomes them. He asks them to help him. Milo says yes.

◆ ◆ ◆

MAN. Splendid, for there are just three tasks. First, I would like to move this pile of sand from here to there. *(Indicates through pantomime[1] a large pile of sand.)* But I'm afraid that all I have is this tiny tweezers. *(Hands it to* MILO, *who begins moving the sand one grain at a time.)* Second, I would like to empty this well and fill that other, but I have no bucket, so you'll have to use this eyedropper. *(Hands it to* TOCK, *who begins to work.)* And finally, I must have a hole in this cliff, and here is a needle to dig it.

◆ ◆ ◆

Time passes. Milo and his friends keep working. They do not get very far. Milo figures out that it will take 837 years to finish the jobs. He tells the man that it does not seem worth it. The man laughs. He tells them that he is the Terrible Trivium. He keeps people busy doing things that are not important.

◆ ◆ ◆

Vocabulary Development

splendid (SPLEN did) *adj.* wonderful
tweezers (TWEEZ erz) *n.* a metal tool used to take out or hold small objects

---

1. pantomime (PAN tuh mym) *n.* performance that uses action and no words.

TAKE NOTES

Activate Prior Knowledge

Describe a challenge you faced that has made you stronger in some way.

_____

_____

Culture Note

Rhyme and Reason are princesses. Children have often enjoyed stories about princesses. *Cinderella* is one such story about a young woman who turns into a princess after a prince rescues her.

Reading Skill

Picture the action to help you remember details and events. What single event or detail do you remember best from Act I, Scene ii?

_____

_____

Literary Analysis

Stage directions help readers picture the action, sounds, and scenery. These words are usually printed in italics between brackets. What do the underlined stage directions tell you about how long Milo's task will take?

_____

Comparing two things means telling how they are alike. How is the Terrible Trivium similar to the Lethargarians from Act I?

_____

_____

_____

Exclamation points tell you where to pause to stress a word or thought. Circle the exclamation points in the bracketed passage. What do they tell you about Humbug's feelings?

_____

_____

The word *scurry* means "to go or move in a hurry." Circle the words near *scurry* that mean the opposite.

Who does the voice say that he is? Circle the answer.

MAN. Think of all the trouble it saves. If you spend all your time doing only the easy and useless jobs, you'll never have time to worry about the important ones which are so difficult. *(Walks toward them whispering.)* Now do come and stay with me. We'll have such fun together.

◆ ◆ ◆

Milo and his friends hear a voice. It tells them to run. They listen to the voice and run. They escape the Terrible Trivium. Then, they fall into a deep pit. They find out that the voice is the Demon of Insincerity. He always gives bad advice. The demon leaves. Milo, Tock, and Humbug get out of the pit. They hurry toward the castle to save the Princesses. Tock sees something chasing them.

◆ ◆ ◆

TOCK. Not just one, I'm afraid. If you want to see what I'm talking about, then turn around. *(They turn around. The stage darkens and hundreds of Yellow Gleaming Eyes can be seen.)*

HUMBUG. Good grief! Do you see how many there are? Hundreds! The Overbearing Know-it-all, the Gross Exaggeration, the Horrible Hopping Hindsight, . . . and look over there! The Triple Demons of Compromise! Let's get out of here! *(Starts to scurry.)* Hurry up, you two! Must you be so slow about everything?

◆ ◆ ◆

The three race toward the castle. At last, they get there. They see a man sleeping on the first step. He has a book, a pen, and a bottle of ink. The man wakes up.

◆ ◆ ◆

SENSES TAKER. Oh, this won't take long. I'm the official Senses Taker and I must have some information before I can take your sense. Now if you'll just tell me: *(Handing them a form to fill. Speaking slowly and deliberately.)* When you were born, where you were born, why you were born, how old you are now, how old you were then, how old you'll be in a little while . . .

◆ ◆ ◆

Milo and his friends try to get by the Senses Taker. The Senses Taker puts a spell on each of them. Milo hears circus music. He stops to listen. An interesting smell makes Tock stop. Humbug hears applause and stops.

◆ ◆ ◆

(MILO *accidentally drops his package of gifts. The Package of Laughter from* DR. DISCHORD *opens and the Sounds of Laughter are heard. After a moment,* MILO, TOCK *and* HUMBUG *join in laughing and the spells are broken. . . .*)

SENSES TAKER. I warned you I was the Senses Taker. I'll steal your sense of Purpose, your sense of Duty, destroy your sense of Proportion—and but for one thing, you'd be helpless yet.

MILO. What's that?

SENSES TAKER. As long as you have the sound of laughter, I cannot take your sense of Humor. Agh! That horrible sense of humor.

◆ ◆ ◆

Milo and his friends see that the demons are catching up. They quickly run away. The demons chase them. At last, Milo and his friends get to the castle. There is no door. There is no way to get inside.

◆ ◆ ◆

REASON. Take your time, Milo, and think about it.

MILO. Ummm, all right . . . just give me a second or two. (*He thinks hard.*)

HUMBUG. I think I feel sick.

MILO. I've got it! Where's that package of presents? (*Opens the package of letters.*) Ah, here it is. (*Takes out the letters and sticks them on the door, spelling:*) E-N-T-R-A-N-C-E. Entrance. Now, let's see. (<u>Rummages</u> *through and spells in smaller letters:*) P-u-s-h. Push. (*He pushes and a*

Vocabulary Development

rummages (RUM ij iz) *v.*   searches for something

© Pearson Education, Inc., publishing as Pearson Prentice Hall.

The Phantom Tollbooth, Act II **263**

Reading Skill

Read the first bracketed passage. How are each of the traps that the Senses Taker sets appropriate for the character? **Compare** the traps to one another?

_____

_____

_____

_____

_____

_____

_____

Reading Check

What breaks the Senses Taker's spell? Circle the answer.

Literary Analysis

What do the **stage directions** in the second bracketed passage tell about how Milo gets the Princesses out of the castle?

_____

_____

_____

_____

_____

The phrase *time flies* usually means "time goes by quickly." It is used differently here. How does this phrase apply to Tock? Underline the sentences that offer a clue to how this phrase is used here.

_____

_____

_____

_____

You tell how two things are different when you **contrast** them. Contrast the views that Milo and Reason have of Milo's bravery.

_____

_____

_____

_____

What might Mathemagician's underlined statement say about the power of words?

_____

_____

_____

_____

door opens. *The* PRINCESSES *come out of the castle. Slowly, the demons ascend*[2] *the stairway.*)

♦   ♦   ♦

There is only one way to escape. Tock carries everyone on his back. Then he jumps. Because "time flies," nobody gets hurt. The demons chase them. Azaz and Mathemagician arrive with their armies. They defeat the demons. The Princesses thank Milo, Tock, and Humbug. Everyone else bows to the heroes.

♦   ♦   ♦

MILO. But we never could have done it without a lot of help.

REASON. That may be true, but you had the courage to try, and what you can do is often a matter of what you *will* do.

AZAZ. That's why there was one very important thing about your quest we couldn't discuss until you returned.

MILO. I remember. What was it?

AZAZ. Very simple. It was impossible!

MATHEMAGICIAN. Completely impossible!

HUMBUG. Do you mean . . . ? (*Feeling faint.*) Oh . . . I think I need to sit down.

AZAZ. Yes, indeed, but if we'd told you then, you might not have gone.

MATHEMAGICIAN. And, as you discovered, many things are possible just as long as you don't know they're impossible.

♦   ♦   ♦

Rhyme and Reason thank the heroes for rescuing them. Milo feels bad for not saving the Princesses earlier. He says he made too many mistakes. The Princesses remind him that it is okay to make mistakes. Mistakes are often the only way to learn. Milo says goodbye to Azaz and Mathemagician. He drives off. Soon he finds himself back in his bedroom. He was only gone for an hour. He starts to examine his books, toys, and other things. He looks at his watch. He is surprised to see that an hour has passed.

---

2. ascend (uh SEND) *v.* to move up; go higher.

The Phantom Tollbooth, Act II

1. **Deduce:** The Terrible Trivium wants Milo, Tock, and Humbug to do "easy and useless" tasks. What will happen if they follow his directions?

   _____

   _____

2. **Draw Conclusions:** What does Milo learn about humor from his meeting with the Senses Taker?

   _____

   _____

3. **Reading Skill: Comparing** and **contrasting** tell how two things are alike and different. Fill in this Venn diagram with details from Act II, Scene ii to compare and contrast the Senses Taker and the Terrible Trivium.

Senses Taker   **Terrible Trivium**

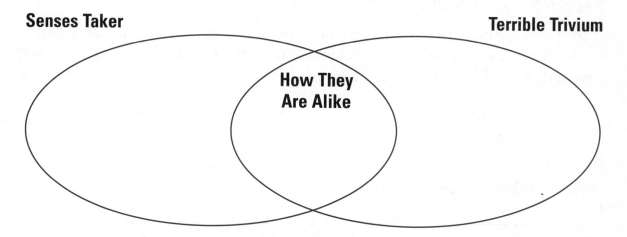

How They
Are Alike

4. **Literary Analysis: Stage directions** help readers understand what the characters in a play are doing. Describe one place in the play where stage directions are needed for understanding what is happening.

   _____

   _____

SUPPORT FOR WRITING AND EXTEND YOUR LEARNING

Writing: Review

Write a **review** of *The Phantom Tollbooth*. Answer the following questions to help you present your opinions in your review.

- Which characters are the most exciting? Why?

_____

_____

_____

- Do any characters become more interesting as you think about them? If so, which characters?

_____

_____

- Which events are the funniest? The most confusing?

_____

_____

_____

Research and Technology: Math Report

Prepare a **math report** on infinity and the largest and smallest numbers. Then create a poster or other graphic that explains what you have learned. Fill in the chart below to come up with ideas for your graphic.

Objects to help show infinity	
Objects to show smallest numbers	
Objects to show largest numbers	
Ways to compare largest and smallest numbers	

Black Cowboy, Wild Horses

People told stories long before there were books to read. People who tell stories aloud follow what is called the **oral tradition**. Most folk tales, fables, myths, legends, folk songs, and fairy tales were once told aloud. Look for these characteristics in stories from the oral tradition:

- A **universal theme** is a message about life that most people understand.

- **Fantasy** is a type of make-believe writing. Fantasy has elements that are not found in real life.

- **Personification** is a special type of language. Writers use personification to give human characteristics to nonhuman subjects. Animals that can talk show personification.

- **Irony** is a surprising event that is the opposite of what you expect. Unexpected endings are called **ironic** endings.

- **Hyperbole** is an exaggeration. An *exaggeration* describes something as being more or less than it really is. "I am so thirsty that I could drink the ocean" is an example of hyperbole. Hyperbole is usually meant to be funny.

- **Dialect** is the form of language spoken by people from a certain place. Storytellers use dialect to make **characters** seem real.

- **Local customs** are the traditions of a group of people. Writers use details about local customs to help build the **setting**. The setting is the time and place of a story's action.

This chart describes the different types of stories found in the oral tradition.

Type of Oral Tradition	Definition	Example
Folk Tales	• entertaining stories that tell about shared ideas of a culture • often have heroes, adventure, magic, or romance • Details change over time. • were later written down	*The Ant and the Dove*
Fables	• brief stories or poems • teach a lesson or moral • usually have animal characters	*The Lion and the Bulls*
Myths	• fictional tales about gods and heroes or natural events • A collection of myths is a culture's **mythology**.	*Arachne*
Legends	• a culture's familiar and traditional stories • often based on fact • change to include more fictional details over time • may become subject of an **allusion**, a reference to a well-known person, place, event, or literary work	*The Legend of Sleepy Hollow*

Black Cowboy, Wild Horses

Julius Lester

Summary Bob Lemmons is a cowboy who tracks a herd of wild horses. He rides his black stallion, Warrior, who knows how to blend in among wild horses. Bob and Warrior fight the wild herd's leader for control of the herd. They lead the herd on an exciting run.

Note-taking Guide

Fill in the cause-and-effect chart to show how Bob and Warrior took over the herd.

Cause

Bob charged at the stallion.

Effect/Cause

Effect/Cause

Effect/Cause

Effect/Cause

Effect

The stallion turned and trotted away.

This story is about a cowboy and horses. Briefly describe a story you know about cowboys or horses.

_____

_____

The word *plain* can be used as a noun meaning "a large open area that is mostly flat and has few trees." It can also be used as an adjective that means "simple and ordinary." How is it used in the underlined sentence? Circle your answer.

Adjective   Noun

Setting is the time and place in a story. What is the setting of this story?

_____

_____

Hyperbole is used to describe something as being more or less than it really is. What is the hyperbole in the bracketed paragraph?

_____

_____

Black Cowboy, Wild Horses
Julius Lester

The story begins as Bob Lemmons rode his black stallion, Warrior, slowly up the hill and then looked back down at the corral. The other cowboys were busy with morning chores. In front of Bob and Warrior, the land was a flat plain, stretching out to the horizon.

Slowly, Bob rode down to the plain. Warrior reared, eager to run. Bob soothed him, promising that soon they would have a chance to run. Now, however, Bob needed to study the ground. Hours later, he saw what he was searching for—the tracks of wild horses, or mustangs. He examined the hoofprints carefully.

◆   ◆   ◆

Some people learned from books. Bob had been a slave and never learned to read words. But he could look at the ground and read what animals had walked on it, their size and weight, when they had passed by, and where they were going. No one he knew could bring in mustangs by themselves, but Bob could make horses think he was one of them—because he was.

◆   ◆   ◆

The tracks showed that eight mares, a colt, and a stallion had passed by two days earlier. Before he joined them, Bob knew he'd have to lose his human scent.

At sunset, it grew cold, but Bob couldn't light a campfire. The mustangs would be able to smell smoke on his clothes. He ate cold food he'd brought along, and then slept.

Early the next morning, he and Warrior were off again, and followed the tracks until

Vocabulary Development

corral (kor AL) *n.*   an enclosed area for keeping animals
mares (STAL yuhn) *n.*   female horses

dusk. Suddenly, lightning flashed across the sky. Bob galloped Warrior to the safety of a ravine. Then, far away, he saw the herd of mustangs. Warrior reared, and the wild stallion seemed to rear in response. Then the hard, heavy rains began.

The rain would have washed away the horses' tracks, but Bob knew that the horses were headed toward the river. Bob followed at daybreak. In the late afternoon, he saw horses approach the water. The stallion looked in Bob's direction and sniffed the air. Bob worried that he had come in too close. If the stallion became alarmed, the herd would gallop away, out of Bob's reach.

◆　◆　◆

The stallion seemed to be looking directly at him. Bob was too far away to be seen, but he did not even blink his eyes, afraid the stallion would hear the sound. Finally the stallion began drinking and the other horses followed. Bob let his breath out slowly. He had been accepted.

◆　◆　◆

Bob followed the herd again the next day. When the horses grazed, he moved forward. When the wild stallion raised his head, Bob stopped. When the herd moved, he and Warrior moved too, slowing closing in.

◆　◆　◆

The mustangs sensed his presence. They thought he was a horse.

So did he.

◆　◆　◆

The next morning, Bob and Warrior gradually joined the herd. The stallion looked at them quickly and then started the herd

---

Vocabulary Development

ravine (ruh VEEN) *n.*   a long, deep hollow in the earth's surface

A *simile* compares two unlike things. A simile uses *like* or *as* to make the comparison. Read the bracketed paragraph. Underline the simile. What is similar about the two things in this simile?

_____

_____

_____

Oral Traditions

A *conflict* is a struggle between opposing forces. A conflict between people or animals is a **universal theme** in literature. Three separate conflicts occur in the text on this page. Write who is involved in each conflict.

_____

_____

_____

_____

Oral Traditions

Folk tales can have heroes. Heroes have special qualities that ordinary people do not have. How is Bob's behavior with Warrior like that of a hero?

_____

_____

_____

_____

running. Bob galloped along with them, hiding from view by lying low in the saddle, against Warrior's back.

As the herd moved slowly along the following day, the colt suddenly fell. Then Bob heard the rattlesnake.

◆　◆　◆

The horses whinnied and pranced nervously, smelling the snake and death among them. Bob saw the rattler, as beautiful as a necklace, sliding silently through the tall grasses. He made no move to kill it. Everything in nature had the right to protect itself, especially when it was afraid.

◆　◆　◆

The colt died quickly. As vultures circled above, the stallion tried to move the herd along, but the colt's mother refused to move. The stallion repeatedly nipped at her, and finally she joined the galloping herd.

Bob knew that it was time to take charge. He and Warrior galloped to the stallion and forced him to stop. The stallion seemed surprised and confused. Bob charged at him. Warrior and the stallion reared at each other, kicking and biting. Then Bob and Warrior charged again and again.

The stallion fought back, biting Warrior's neck. Angrily, Warrior reared and kicked the stallion hard.

◆　◆　◆

Still maintaining his balance, Warrior struck again and again. The mustang stallion cried out in pain. Warrior pushed hard against the stallion. The stallion lost his footing and fell to the earth. Warrior rose, neighing triumphantly, his front legs pawing as if seeking for the rungs on which he could climb a ladder into the sky.

The mustang scrambled to his feet, beaten. He snorted weakly. When Warrior made as if to attack again, the stallion turned, whinnied weakly, and trotted away.

◆　◆　◆

Bob led the herd slowly at first, gaining speed only when he was sure that the horses would follow him.

♦ ♦ ♦

Throughout that day and the next he rode with the horses. For Bob there was only the bulging of the horses' dark eyes, the quivering of their flesh, the rippling of muscles and bending of bones in their bodies. He was now sky and plains and grass and river and horse.

♦ ♦ ♦

Finally, Bob led them on one last gallop across the plains, up over the hill where he and Warrior had started out, and down toward home. Then he stopped Warrior and let the wild horses stream ahead into the corral. The other cowboys shouted and slammed the gate shut.

Bob and Warrior rode back to the top of the hill. As they stared out over the plains, Warrior reared and whinnied.

♦ ♦ ♦

"I know," Bob whispered. "I know. Maybe someday."

Maybe someday they would ride with the mustangs, ride to that forever place where land and sky kissed, and then ride on. Maybe someday.

© Pearson Education, Inc., publishing as Pearson Prentice Hall.

TAKE NOTES

Oral Traditions

This story has elements of a **legend**. In a legend, facts become exaggerated over time. Read the first bracketed paragraph. How does the paragraph make Bob seem to be a legend?

_____

_____

_____

_____

Oral Traditions

Personification is used when an author gives human qualities to a nonhuman subject. Read the second bracketed paragraph. Circle the example of personification.

Culture Note

Cowboys helped the cattle industry grow in the western part of the United States during the 1800s. They also became part of American folklore. Many books and movies depict the lives of cowboys.

Reading Check

Where does Bob finally lead the wild mustangs? Circle the answer in the text.

Oral Tradition

1. **Infer:** Bob is very careful about how he follows the mustangs. What danger does Bob face in coming close to the mustangs too soon?

_____

_____

2. **Compare:** Bob and Warrior are very close. Bob has a deep understanding of Warrior. Why does it seem that Warrior's goals or dreams are the same as Bob's?

_____

_____

3. **Oral Tradition:** A **legend** is a story that has changed over time. The once-true events of the story have been exaggerated. List qualities about Bob that make him seem real. Then, list qualities that exaggerate his abilities and make him a **legend**. Use this diagram.

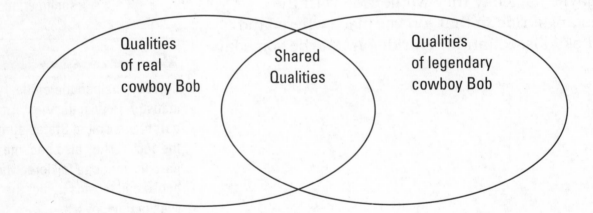

4. **Oral Tradition:** A **universal theme** is a message about life that people in most cultures understand. What is the **universal theme** in this **folk tale**?

_____

_____

RESEARCH THE AUTHOR

Reading

Follow these steps to gather information for a **reading** of passages from some of Julius Lester's books.

- Search the Internet to find background information about Julius Lester and his books. Begin by finding his home page. Type the following in your browser's address box: http://members.authorsguild.net/juliuslester/. Press the enter key. Click on the "My Books" link to see a list of Lester's books and a brief description of each book. Also, select a search engine for further research. Type "*Julius Lester*" AND *books* or "*Julius Lester*" AND "*folk tales*" in the search box. Choose reliable sites when the results come up. These include sites about the author and the sources used to make the site. Write the titles of books that interest you and a description of each book.

Book: _____

_____

Book: _____

_____

Book: _____

_____

- Go to the library. Find a computer and the online catalogue. Select an author search. Type *Lester, Julius* in the search box. Press the enter key. A list of Lester's books will come up. Write the titles of the books you want and the information that will help you find each book. Then find the books on the shelf.

- Read as many of Lester's stories as interest you. Look for interesting **dialect**. Dialect is the language spoken in a particular region. Choose one of Lester's books to read. Then read the entire book.

- Select some passages that interest you. Practice reading the passages aloud.

- Watch the video interview with Julius Lester. Then review your source material. Use this information to help prepare for your reading.

The Tiger Who Would be King • The Ant and the Dove • The Lion and the Bulls • A Crippled Boy

READING SKILL

A **cause** is an event, an action, or a feeling that leads to a result. The result is called an **effect**. Sometimes an effect can have more than one cause. **Reread** important passages in the work to figure out the relationship between an event and its causes. Use this chart to record the events and actions that produce an effect.

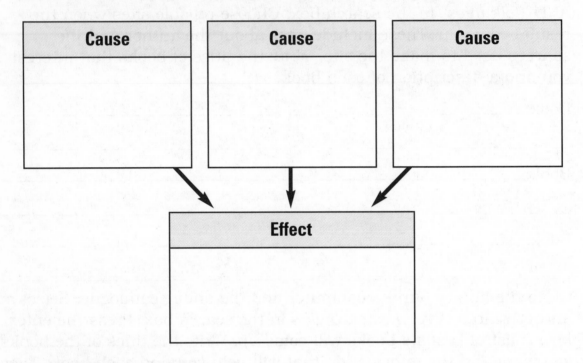

LITERARY ANALYSIS

Fables and folk tales are part of the oral tradition. The oral tradition is the tradition of passing songs, stories, and poems from generation to generation by word of mouth.

- **Fables** are short stories that teach a lesson or contain a moral. They often have animal characters.

- **Folk tales** have heroes, adventure, magic, and romance. These stories often entertain while teaching a lesson.

Some fables and folk tales have **ironic**, or surprising, endings. The endings are ironic because they do not turn out as you expect.

The Tiger Who Would Be King • The Ant and the Dove

Summary "The Tiger Who Would Be King" tells the story of a fight among the animals to show that sometimes no one wins. "The Ant and the Dove" shows that a good deed can be repaid at an unexpected time.

Reading/Writing Connection

Complete this paragraph by describing a story that teaches a lesson.

The fable about honesty teaches people to <u>adapt</u> _____.

Sometimes people lie to <u>achieve</u> _____. You are never sure

how someone will <u>react</u> when you _____.

Note-taking Guide

Use this chart to list the actions taken by the characters in "The Tiger Who Would Be King" and "The Ant and the Dove." Then, list why each character takes the actions.

Character	Action taken	Motivation, or why the action is taken
Tiger	Fights the lion	Wants to be king of the beasts
Lion		
Dove		
Ant		

Describe a time when you wanted something so badly that you thought you would do anything to get it.

_____

_____

A story is clearer when you know who is speaking. Each time a character speaks, the words will be in quotation marks (""). A new paragraph starts when a new character begins speaking. Read the bracketed passage. Circle the words spoken by the tigress. Underline the words spoken by the tiger.

A **cause** is an event, an action, or a feeling that produces a result, or an **effect**. What causes Leo to defend his crown?

_____

In the story, *struggle* is used as a noun meaning "conflict." *Struggle* can also be used as a verb meaning "to fight." Write a sentence, using *struggle* as a verb.

The Tiger Who Would Be King
James Thurber

One morning the tiger woke up in the jungle and told his mate that he was king of beasts.

"Leo, the lion, is king of beasts," she said.

"We need a change," said the tiger. "The creatures are crying for a change."

The tigress listened but she could hear no crying, except that of her cubs.

"I'll be king of beasts by the time the moon rises," said the tiger. "It will be a yellow moon with black stripes, in my honor."

"Oh, sure," said the tigress as she went to look after her young, one of whom, a male, very like his father, had got an imaginary thorn in his paw.

The tiger <u>prowled</u> through the jungle till he came to the lion's den. "Come out," he roared, "and greet the king of beasts! The king is dead, long live the king!"

Inside the den, the lioness woke her mate. "The king is here to see you," she said.

"What king?" he inquired, sleepily.

"The king of beasts," she said.

"I am the king of beasts," roared Leo, and he charged out of the den to defend his crown against the pretender.

It was a terrible fight, and it lasted until the setting of the sun. All the animals of the jungle joined in, some taking the side of the tiger and others the side of the lion. Every creature from the aardvark to the zebra took part in the struggle to overthrow the lion or to <u>repulse</u> the tiger, and some did not know which they were fighting for, and some fought for both, and some fought whoever was nearest, and some fought for the sake of fighting.

Vocabulary Development

prowled (prowld) *v.* moved around quietly and secretly
repulse (ri PULS) *v.* drive back; repel an attack

"What are we fighting for?" someone asked the aardvark.

"The old order," said the aardvark.

"What are we dying for?" someone asked the zebra.

"The new order," said the zebra.

When the moon rose, fevered and gibbous,[1] it shone upon a jungle in which nothing stirred except a macaw[2] and a cockatoo,[3] screaming in horror. All the beasts were dead except the tiger, and his days were numbered and his time was ticking away. He was monarch of all he surveyed, but it didn't seem to mean anything.

MORAL: You can't very well be king of beasts if there aren't any.

The Ant and the Dove
RUSSIAN FOLK TALE
Leo Tolstoy

A thirsty ant went to the stream to drink. Suddenly it got caught in a whirlpool and was almost carried away.

At that moment a dove was passing by with a twig in its beak. The dove dropped the twig for the tiny insect to grab hold of. So it was that the ant was saved.

A few days later a hunter was about to catch the dove in his net. When the ant saw what was happening, it walked right up to the man and bit him on the foot. Startled, the man dropped the net. And the dove, thinking that you never can tell how or when a kindness may be repaid, flew away.

Vocabulary Development

startled (STAHRT uhld) *adj.* surprised

---

1. **gibbous** (GIB uhs) *adj.* more than half but less than completely illuminated.
2. **macaw** (muh KAW) *n.* bright-colored, harsh-voiced parrot of Central or South America.
3. **cockatoo** (kahk uh TOO) *n.* crested parrot with white plumage tinged with yellow or pink.

TAKE NOTES

Build English Skills

The word *and* can connect two complete thoughts in one sentence. The two thoughts can be written as two separate sentences. Rewrite the underlined sentence as two sentences.

_____

_____

Literary Analysis

A **folktale** often has heroes, adventure, magic, and romance to tell a story that teaches a lesson. Who is the hero of "The Ant and the Dove"?

_____

_____

Culture Note

Fables and folktales from other countries have become part of the American oral tradition. Families from around the world brought stories from their home countries when they came to the United States.

Reading Check

How did the ant save the dove? Underline the text that tells you.

The Tiger Who Would Be King • The Ant and the Dove

1. **Apply:** Some animals in "The Tiger Who Would Be King" fight without thinking about the outcome of their actions. What human qualities does Thurber show in these animals?

   _____

   _____

2. **Infer:** The dove in "The Ant and the Dove" drops a twig for the ant. How does this save the ant?

   _____

   _____

3. **Reading Skill:** "The Tiger Who Would Be King" ends in a fight among all of the animals in the jungle. This fight is an effect, or result. List two **causes,** or reasons, of the fight in the jungle.

   _____

   _____

4. **Literary Analysis: Fables** and **folk tales** share some of the same elements. Use this chart to describe the elements of fables and folk tales in the two stories. List characters from each tale. Then, describe the moral or lesson that each tale teaches.

Title	Characters	Moral or Lesson
The Tiger Who Would Be King		
The Ant and the Dove		

SUPPORT FOR WRITING AND EXTEND YOUR LEARNING

Writing: Fable

Write a **fable** that teaches the same lesson as either "The Tiger Who Would Be King" or "The Ant and the Dove." Answer the following questions to help you write your fable.

- What is the lesson that you want your readers to learn?

_____

- Who are the characters in your fable?

_____

- How do the characters get in trouble?

_____

_____

- How do the characters learn a lesson?

_____

_____

Listening and Speaking: Oral Report

Prepare an **oral report** on the life of either James Thurber or Leo Tolstoy. Complete the following chart to prepare your oral report.

Author:		
Childhood Events	**Life as a Writer**	**Photos or Images**
Other pieces to read by this author:		

The Lion and the Bulls • A Crippled Boy

Summary A lion spreads rumors to break apart a group of bulls in "The Lion and the Bulls." "A Crippled Boy" shows a lonely, disabled boy with a great skill. His skill earns him a place at the king's palace.

Reading/Writing Connection

Complete each sentence to describe ways that a person can achieve a goal.

1. She must <u>rely</u> on _____.

2. She must learn to <u>focus</u> _____.

3. She will need _____ to <u>cooperate</u> with her.

Note-taking Guide

Use this chart to record details from "The Lion and the Bulls" and "A Crippled Boy."

Character	What problem does he face?	How does he solve his problem?
Lion		
Theo		

The Lion and the Bulls • A Crippled Boy

1. **Infer:** Aesop gives human qualities to his animal characters in "The Lion and the Bulls." Describe these human qualities.

   _____

   _____

2. **Analyze:** Name one way in which Theo from "A Crippled Boy" benefits from developing his talent.

   _____

   _____

3. **Reading Skill:** A **cause** is an event or action that results in an **effect**. The bulls' moving away from one another in "The Lion and the Bulls" is a cause that leads to an effect. What is this effect?

   _____

   _____

4. **Literary Analysis:** Use this chart to identify the elements of **fable** and **folk tale** in the two stories.

Title	Characters	Moral or Lesson
The Lion and the Bulls		
A Crippled Boy		

Writing: Fable

Write a **fable** that teaches the same lesson as either "The Lion and the Bulls" or "A Crippled Boy." Answer the following questions to help you write your fable.

• What is the lesson that you want your readers to learn?

_____

• Who are the characters in your fable?

_____

• How do the characters get in trouble?

_____

_____

• How do the characters learn a lesson?

_____

_____

Research and Technology: Annotated List

Write an **annotated list** of stories that are retellings of "The Lion and the Bulls" and "A Crippled Boy." Use the chart to describe the retellings you find.

Tales	Titles of retellings	What characters are different?	What events are different?
The Lion and the Bulls			
A Crippled Boy			

Prologue from The Whale Rider • Arachne

READING SKILL

A **cause** is an event, an action, or a feeling. A cause makes something happen. An **effect** is what happens. An effect can become the cause of another event.

Look for clue words such as *because*, *so*, and *as a result*. These words signal a cause-and-effect relationship. **Ask questions** to help you understand the cause-and-effect relationships. Some questions to ask are

- "What happened?"

- "Why did this happen?"

LITERARY ANALYSIS

Myths are stories about the actions of gods or heroes. Every culture has its own myths. Myths can do many things. They can tell how the world began. They can explain something in nature, such as thunder. A myth might teach a lesson. It might state a value, such as courage. Use this chart to analyze myths as you read.

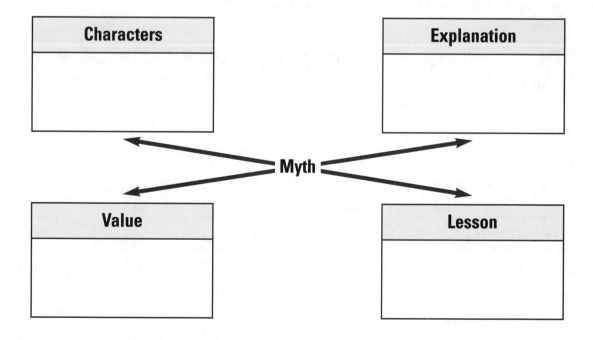

Prologue from The Whale Rider

Witi Ihimaera

Summary This myth explains the beginnings of the Maori people of New Zealand. It tells of a man who rides a whale through the ocean and onto land. It also explores the wonders of the land and the ocean.

Reading/Writing Connection

Complete these sentences. Describe animals that make you think of strength and greatness.

1. Seals project _____.

2. A lion may display the important trait of _____.

3. Gazelles demonstrate _____.

Note-taking Guide:

Use this chart to record details about the selection.

What do both the land and sea feel?	**Where** do the fairy people go?	**When** is the first sighting made?	**How** does the flying fish know that the time has come?	**Who** comes to the land on the whale?
Both land and sea feel a great emptiness and yearning.				

Prologue from The Whale Rider

1. **Analyze:** The land and sea are said to have feelings of yearning and emptiness. What effect do these descriptions have on the story?

   _____

   _____

2. **Infer:** Why are the land and sea excited when the Ancients arrive?

   _____

   _____

3. **Reading Skill:** A **cause** makes something happen. An **effect** is what happens. Complete this chart with causes and effects in *The Whale Rider* prologue.

Causes	Effects
The land and sea feel a great emptiness.	
	Flying fish leap to look beyond the horizon.
The whale rider says a prayer over the last spear.	

4. **Literary Analysis: Myths** are stories that teach lessons or tell how the world began. What is taught in this myth?

   _____

   _____

SUPPORT FOR WRITING AND EXTEND YOUR LEARNING

Writing: Essay

Write a short **essay**. Compare your experience of waiting for something exciting to happen with the sense of anticipation and joy expressed in the selection. Answer the following questions to help you organize your comparison. Use these notes to help you complete the essay.

- What experience will you write about?

  _____

- How will you introduce this experience in your essay?

  _____

- How will you compare your feelings with the feelings expressed in *The Whale Rider* prologue?

  _____

- Compare the lesson you learned from your experience with what is learned in *The Whale Rider* prologue. How will you relate the two in your essay?

  _____

Listening and Speaking: An Oral Report

Prepare an **oral report** about the types of whales found off the coast of New Zealand. Use this chart to help you gather information. Use your notes to help you complete your report.

	Whale 1:	Whale 2:
Appearance		
Diet		
Life span		
Community living		
Babies		

Arachne

Olivia E. Coolidge

Summary This myth describes how spiders came to be. In this tale, a young girl named Arachne weaves a beautiful cloth. She brags because she is proud of her cloth. Her bragging makes the goddess Athene angry. Athene punishes Arachne for her pride.

Reading/Writing Connection

Complete this paragraph to describe lessons people can learn through life experiences.

She faced a <u>challenge</u> when _____. She tried to

<u>convince</u> _____. She began to <u>protest</u> when

_____.

Note-taking Guide

Use this chart to record details about Arachne and Athene from the myth.

	Arachne	Athene
Who she is	Young Greek woman	Greek goddess of wisdom, skills, and warfare
What she looks like		
How she acts		

Think about a time when someone you knew was bragging. How did this person's bragging make other people feel?

_____

_____

Myths are fictional tales that describe the actions of gods or heroes. Read the bracketed paragraph. Underline a clue that tells you that this story is a myth.

Most regular verbs in English end in -ed in the past tense: for example, *learned* is the past tense of *learn*. Many common verbs are irregular, however. For example, *came* is the past tense of *come*. Circle the irregular past tenses of *spin*, *weave*, and *go*.

Arachne
Olivia E. Coolidge

The main character in this story is Arachne, a young Greek woman. Arachne was not rich or famous or beautiful. She came from a small village where her father was known for his ability to dye, or color, wool into beautiful colors. But Arachne was more talented than her father. She spun the wool into soft thread and then wove it into beautiful cloth on a loom.

◆　◆　◆

Arachne was small and pale from much working. Her eyes were light and her hair was a dusty brown, yet she was quick and graceful, and her fingers . . . went so fast that it was hard to follow their flickering movement. So soft and even was her thread, so fine her cloth, so gorgeous her <u>embroidery</u>, that soon her products were known all over Greece. No one had ever seen the like of them before.

◆　◆　◆

People came from far away to watch her. They said that the goddess Athene must have taught Arachne her great skill. But Arachne was very proud and did not like people to think she learned her skill from anyone else, even from a goddess. She told them that Athene herself could not weave cloth more beautiful than her own.

One day a poor old woman warned Arachne that it was not wise to say that she was better than one of the gods. The old woman told Arachne that she should be satisfied to be the best human spinner and

---

Vocabulary Development

embroidery (im BROY der ee) *n.*　design stitched on cloth

weaver. But Arachne was angry and yelled at the old woman. She told her that she had challenged Athene to a spinning and weaving contest, but Athene was not brave enough to come.

◆　◆　◆

At these words the old woman threw down her staff and stood erect. The wondering onlookers saw her grow tall and fair and stand <u>clad</u> in long robes of <u>dazzling</u> white. They were terribly afraid as they realized that they stood in the presence of Athene. Arachne herself flushed red for a moment, for she had never really believed that the goddess would hear her.

◆　◆　◆

But Arachne was also proud and stubborn, so she led Athene to a loom where they began their spinning and weaving contest. Both of them created beautiful cloth, but the goddess moved faster.

Athene wove a picture into her cloth as a warning to Arachne. The picture showed the goddess in the middle. In the corners were pictures of awful things that had happened to humans who had challenged the gods. Athene finished weaving and stepped back. When Arachne saw Athene's picture, she became angry. In her own cloth she created a picture of evil things the gods and goddesses had done in the past.

◆　◆　◆

When the goddess saw this insult glowing in bright colors on Arachne's loom, she did not wait while the cloth was judged, but stepped forward, her gray eyes blazing with anger, and tore Arachne's work across. Then she struck Arachne across the face. Arachne stood there a

---

Vocabulary Development

clad (klad) *v.*   dressed
dazzling (DAZ ling) *adv.*   bright; very light

TAKE NOTES

Literary Analysis

Myths often teach about values. What value gets Arachne into trouble?

_____

_____

How did the Greeks probably feel about this value?

_____

_____

_____

Reading Skill

What **causes** Athene to become angry?

_____

_____

_____

Read Fluently

When writers want to combine two sentences, they often use a comma and a conjunction such as *so, and,* or *but.* Remember this as you read this page. Circle two examples in which a comma and a conjunction are used to combine two sentences.

Reading Check

Who is the old woman? Circle the answer in the text.

The word *insult* can be used as a noun meaning "a rude or offensive remark or action." It can also be used as a verb that means "to say or do something that offends someone." How is it used in the underlined passage? Circle your answer.

Verb   Noun

What happened when Arachne tried to hang herself? Underline the text that tells you.

Like Arachne, many Americans are proud of their accomplishments. They value the hard work they have done to achieve their goals.

According to this myth, where do spiders come from? Underline the sentence that tells you.

moment, struggling with anger, fear, and pride. "I will not live under this insult," she cried, and seizing the rope from the wall, she made a noose and would have hanged herself.

The goddess touched the rope and touched the maiden. "Live on, wicked girl," she said. "Live on and spin, both you and your descendants. When men look at you they may remember that it is not wise to strive with Athene."

◆ ◆ ◆

Arachne's body began to change. The people soon saw a small dusty brown spider hanging on a thin thread. All spiders come from Arachne. When Greeks saw spiders, they remembered that it was not wise for humans to say they are equal to the gods.

Vocabulary Development

noose (noos) *n.*   loop of rope
descendants (di SEN duhnts) *n.*   people who are related to a particular person who lived long ago

---

Arachne

1. **Analyze:** Arachne refuses to take the old woman's advice. What does this tell you about Arachne?

   _____

   _____

2. **Infer:** What is Athene trying to do when she first comes to Arachne?

   _____

   _____

3. **Reading Skill:** A **cause** is an event or a feeling that makes something happen. And **effect** is what happens. Complete the chart to show causes and effects found in "Arachne."

Causes	Effects
Arachne challenges Athene.	
	Arachne's design shows unworthy actions performed by the gods.
Athene touches the rope and touches Arachne.	

4. **Literary Analysis: Myths** can be used to teach people beliefs and values. What values are taught in this myth?

   _____

   _____

SUPPORT FOR WRITING AND EXTEND YOUR LEARNING

Writing: Essay

Write a brief **essay** about the differences between learning lessons from stories and learning lessons from experience. Answer the following questions to help you organize your essay. Use these notes to help you complete the essay.

- What lessons from your experiences will you write about?

  _____

- How will you introduce these lessons in your essay?

  _____

- How will you compare these lessons with lessons learned from stories?

  _____

- Which do you believe is better: learning a lesson from a story or learning a lesson from experience? Explain your answer.

  _____

  _____

Research and Technology: Report

Prepare a written **report** about Greek gods and goddesses. Answer the following questions for each god or goddess you choose.
Use your notes to help you prepare your report.

- What words can be used to describe this god or goddess?

  _____

- What symbols are used to represent this god or goddess?

  _____

- What words in the English language sound like the name of this god or goddess?

  _____

Cause-and-Effect Articles

ABOUT CAUSE-AND-EFFECT ARTICLES

A **cause-and-effect article** explains connections between events that bring about other events. You can find these articles in newspapers, magazines, and textbooks. Most cause-and-effect articles have the following characteristics:

- an explanation of one or more causes and effects
- facts, statistics, and details to support the explanation
- clear organization
- words that show connections among details

READING SKILL

Understanding the **organizational structure** will help you understand the article. The organizational structure is the way the writing is put together. Many articles are organized to show cause and effect. Ask yourself, "How are the ideas in this piece of writing connected to one another?" as you read. Cause is the reason behind an event. Effect is the result produced by the cause.

These steps will help you identify the causes and effects in an article:

1. Identify the main event or effect.
2. Identify other causes and effects.

Use this chart to help you track causes and effects in the article.

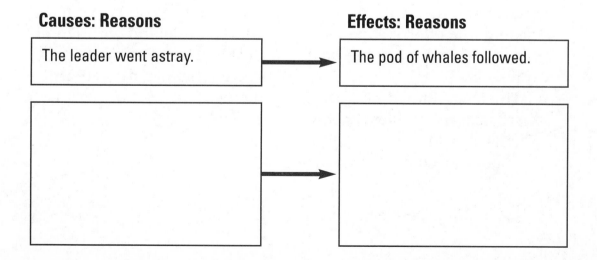

Causes: Reasons

The leader went astray.

Effects: Reasons

The pod of whales followed.

36 Beached Whales Die in St. Martin

By Marvin Hokstam, Associated Press

MARIGOT, St. Martin—Thirty six whales beached themselves on the coast of this Caribbean island and died within hours despite the efforts of people who tried to push some back out to sea.

The short-finned pilot whales were believed to have beached themselves Monday night, and by noon Tuesday all were dead.

The animals were found before dawn by a man on his way to a dump in the French Caribbean territory, which shares an island with Dutch St. Maarten. Residents and tourists later gathered around the whales, which were up to 15 feet long.

People were able to push two whales back into the water, but they returned and beached themselves again, appearing exhausted, said Paul Ellinger, of the St. Maarten Nature Foundation. He said it seemed the whales had become disoriented.

"What's clear is that they got off course. What caused them to go off course? We'll have to check," Ellinger said. "It could be all kinds of reasons: the temperature of the water, their sonar system. It could have been anything."

Short-finned pilot whales usually swim in pods, and when a leader goes astray the entire pod often follows, Ellinger said.

Biologists were keeping three carcasses to investigate.

The whales covered the beach along the shallow Grand Cailles Bay, the mouth of which is fringed with coral reefs. The whales bore injuries apparently sustained when they ran aground.

French police arrived Tuesday morning and closed off the spot as workers dug beach-side graves to bury the remaining whales.

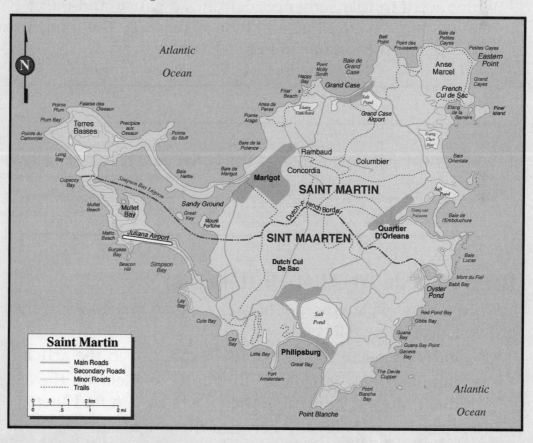

THINKING ABOUT THE CAUSE-AND-EFFECT ARTICLE

1. What is one possible reason that two of the whales beached themselves again?

   _____

   _____

2. Why do you think people want to understand the cause of the whales' death?

   _____

   _____

READING SKILL

3. Which word in this sentence identifies a cause-and-effect relationship? "It could be all kinds of reasons: the temperature of the water, their sonar system." Explain.

   _____

   _____

4. What is the possible cause of the beached whales' injuries?

   _____

   _____

TIMED WRITING: EXPLANATION (15 minutes)

Write a brief explanation of how one cause presented in the article led to many effects.

- Begin by choosing a cause that is explained in the article.
- Reread the article to look for the multiple effects of the cause you have chosen. Underline the effects as you find them.
- Describe the relationship between the single cause and the multiple effects.

He Lion, Bruh Bear, and Bruh Rabbit • Why the Tortoise's Shell Is Not Smooth

READING SKILL

Your **purpose** for reading is the reason you read a text. You may choose to read because of a purpose you have before you read. Sometimes your purpose depends on the kind of text you will read.

Setting a purpose helps you focus your reading. You might set a purpose to do the following:

- learn about a subject

- gain understanding

- take action

- read for enjoyment

Preview the text before you begin to read. Previewing will give you a clue to what lies ahead. It will also help you set a purpose. Use this chart to record details as you preview the text.

Text Details	What the Details Suggest About the Text
Title	
Pictures	
Beginnings of paragraphs	

LITERARY ANALYSIS

Writers use **personification** to give human qualities, such as speech, to nonhuman subjects. Personification is often used in folk tales to give human qualities to animal characters. The actions of the animal characters can be used to show human qualities, behavior, or problems in a funny way.

He Lion, Bruh Bear, . . . • Why the Tortoise's Shell . . .

He Lion, Bruh Bear, and Bruh Rabbit

Virginia Hamilton

Summary He Lion scares the animals when he roars. Bruh Bear and Bruh Rabbit try to get he Lion to calm down. They tell him that Man is the king of the forest. He Lion does not believe them. They take him to see Man. Man does something that makes he Lion be quiet.

Reading/Writing Connection

Complete each sentence to describe human qualities or problems that could be assigned to a lion, a bear, and a rabbit.

1. A lion will always <u>display</u> _____ near other animals.

2. A bear will usually <u>demonstrate</u> _____.

3. People usually think a rabbit will <u>exhibit</u> _____.

Note-taking Guide

Fill in this chart to describe each character in the story.

Character	He Lion	Bruh Bear	Bruh Rabbit	Man
Details about the character	He Lion roars loudly and scares the small animals. He thinks that he is king of the forest.			

He Lion, Bruh Bear, and Bruh Rabbit

1. **Infer:** Bruh Bear and Bruh Rabbit are bothered by what he Lion does. What do Bruh Bear and Bruh Rabbit think of he Lion?

   _____

   _____

2. **Draw Conclusions:** Think about he Lion's behavior. What lesson does this story appear to teach by showing his behavior?

   _____

   _____

3. **Reading Skill:** Your **purpose** for reading is the reason for reading a text. What was your purpose for reading this folk tale?

   _____

4. **Literary Analysis: Personification** is used to give human qualities to nonhuman characters. Use the chart below to analyze the personification of he Lion. First list the ways in which he Lion behaves like an animal. Then list the ways in which he Lion behaves like a human.

Character's Name: he Lion	
Animal Qualities:	**Human Qualities:**

SUPPORT FOR WRITING AND EXTEND YOUR LEARNING

Writing: Invitation

Write an **invitation** to the animals' "sit-down talk" at the beginning of the story. Answer the following questions to help you include details in your invitation.

- List a reason for holding the meeting that all of the animals will understand.

_____

_____

- Everyone at the meeting should have a chance to speak about his or her concerns. How would you organize the talk so that this can happen?

_____

_____

Listening and Speaking: Dramatic Reading

Present a **dramatic reading** of the scene in which he Lion, Bruh Bear, and Bruh Rabbit search for Man. Fill in the spaces in the chart with information about how each character will speak.

he Lion	Bruh Bear	Bruh Rabbit
Tone of voice	Tone of voice	Tone of voice
Speed of speech	Speed of speech	Speed of speech
Level of loudness	Level of loudness	Level of loudness
Words to stress	Words to stress	Words to stress

Why the Tortoise's Shell Is Not Smooth

Chinua Achebe

Summary All of the birds are invited to a feast in the sky. The hungry, clever tortoise wants to go along. He gets the birds to give him feathers so that he can fly. Tortoise figures out a way to eat the best food before the birds can get to it. The angry birds take back their feathers. Tortoise must figure out how to land softly.

Reading/Writing Connection

Complete each sentence to explain why it is important to have complete information when making a decision.

1. People need _____ to <u>evaluate</u> their choices.

2. A person should try to <u>confirm</u> key information _____.

3. Someone could <u>distort</u> _____ with incorrect facts.

Note-taking Guide

Fill in this chart with the events that lead to Tortoise's broken shell.

First	Second	Third	Fourth	Last
The birds are invited to a feast in the sky.				Tortoise breaks his shell when he falls to Earth.

Stories grow and change as they are told over and over again. List ways that you have added to a story when you retold it.

_____

_____

_____

Personification means giving an animal or an object human qualities. Circle examples of personification in the bracketed paragraph. What does this tell you about Tortoise?

_____

_____

Your **purpose** for reading is the reason that you read a text. What purpose for reading does the story's title present?

_____

_____

Why does Tortoise want to go to the feast? Underline the text that tells you.

Why the Tortoise's Shell Is Not Smooth

Chinua Achebe

Have you ever been invited to a feast? Do you remember which foods you enjoyed the most? In "Why the Tortoise's Shell Is Not Smooth," a cunning tortoise tricks his friends the birds and eats a feast in the sky that was meant to be theirs.

As the story begins, Ekwefi starts to tell the story about the tortoise to her daughter, Ezinma:

♦ ♦ ♦

Low voices, broken now and again by singing, reached Okonkwo from his wives' huts as each woman and her children told folk stories. Ekwefi and her daughter, Ezinma, sat on a mat on the floor. It was Ekwefi's turn to tell a story.

"Once upon a time," she began, "all the birds were invited to a feast in the sky. They were very happy and began to prepare themselves for the great day. They painted their bodies with red cam wood[1] and drew beautiful patterns on them with dye.

"Tortoise saw all these preparations and soon discovered what it all meant. Nothing that happened in the world of the animals ever escaped his notice; he was full of cunning."

♦ ♦ ♦

There is a food shortage and Tortoise has not eaten a good meal for two months. He plans how he will go to the feast in the sky.

♦ ♦ ♦

"But he had no wings," said Ezinma.

"Be patient," replied her mother. "That is the story. Tortoise had no wings, but he went to the birds and asked to be allowed to go with them.

---

1. **red cam** (kam) **wood** hard West African wood that makes a red dye.

"We know you too well,' said the birds when they had heard him. 'You are full of cunning and you are ungrateful. If we allow you to come with us you will soon begin your <u>mischief</u>.'

"You do not know me,' said Tortoise. 'I am a changed man. I have learned that a man who makes trouble for others is also making it for himself.'

"Tortoise had a sweet tongue, and within a short time all the birds agreed that he was a changed man, and they each gave him a feather, with which he made two wings.

◆　◆　◆

At last the great day comes. Tortoise is very happy as he and the birds fly away together. The birds choose Tortoise to speak for the party because he is a great orator. He tells the birds that when people are invited to a great feast, they take new names for the occasion. None of the birds have heard of this custom. But they know that Tortoise knows a lot about the customs of different peoples. So they all take new names. Tortoise takes the name *All of you*. Finally they arrive in the sky and their hosts are happy to see them.

◆　◆　◆

"After kola nuts[2] had been presented and eaten, the people of the sky set before their guests the most <u>delectable</u> dishes Tortoise had ever seen or dreamed of. The soup was brought out hot from the fire and in the very pot in which

Vocabulary Development

mischief (MIS chif) *n.*　bad behavior
delectable (di LEK tuh buhl) *adj.*　delicious; delightful

---

2. kola nuts the seeds of the African cola tree. These seeds contain caffeine and are used to make soft drinks and medicines.

TAKE NOTES

Reading Skill

Readers try to figure out what a story is about when they **preview the text**. Preview this page by looking at the beginning of each paragraph. What do you think will happen in this part of the story?

_____

_____

Culture Note

Table manners have received a great deal of attention in America. Emily Post wrote a book on table manners in 1922. It tells readers how to hold eating utensils and how to behave at a meal.

_____

_____

Literary Analysis

Personification includes giving human actions and behaviors to animal characters. Circle the text that shows how gullible, or easily fooled, the birds are.

Reading Check

Why is Tortoise chosen to speak for the group? Circle the text that tells you.

How would you react to the underlined sentence if you were one of the birds?

_____

_____

Writers use single quotation marks (') to show quotations within quotations. For example, "She said, 'I love sailing,' and I believed her." Circle the single quotation marks in the first bracketed paragraph. Who is Ekwefi quoting?

_____

A *prepositional phrase* is a group of words that begins with a preposition and includes a noun or a pronoun. Some common prepositions are *for, to,* and *on.* For example: Sally needs to go *to the store.* The prepositional phrase tells the reader where Sally needs to go. Circle three prepositional phrases in the second bracketed paragraph.

it had been cooked. It was full of meat and fish. Tortoise began to sniff aloud. There was pounded yam and also yam pottage[3] cooked with palm oil and fresh fish. There were also pots of palm wine. When everything had been set before the guests, one of the people of the sky came forward and tasted a little from each pot. He then invited the birds to eat. But Tortoise jumped to his feet and asked: 'For whom have you prepared this feast?"

"For all of you,' replied the man.

"Tortoise turned to the birds and said: 'You remember that my name is *All of you.* The custom here is to serve the spokesman first and the others later. They will serve you when I have eaten.'

♦ ♦ ♦

Tortoise eats the best parts of all the food and drinks two pots of palm wine. His body grows fat and fills out his shell. The birds grumble angrily. Some peck at the bones Tortoise has thrown on the floor. Others are too angry to eat. The birds get ready to fly home. Before they leave, each one takes back the feather he has lent to Tortoise. Now Tortoise has no wings to fly home. He asks the birds to take a message to his wife. Parrot, who is more angry than the others, agrees to take the message.

♦ ♦ ♦

"Tell my wife,' said Tortoise, 'to bring out all the soft things in my house and cover the compound[4] with them so that I can jump down from the sky without very great danger.'

"Parrot promised to deliver the message, and then flew away. But when he reached Tortoise's house he told his wife to bring out all the hard things in the house. And so she brought out her

---

3. **yam** (yam) **pottage** (PAHT ij) *n.* thick stew made of sweet potatoes.
4. **compound** (KAHM pownd) *n.* grounds surrounded by buildings.

husband's hoes, <u>machetes</u>, spears, guns, and even his cannon. Tortoise looked down from the sky and saw his wife bringing things out, but it was too far to see what they were. When all seemed ready, he let himself go. He fell and fell and fell until he began to fear that he would never stop falling. And then like the sound of his cannon he crashed on the compound."

"Did he die?" asked Ezinma.

"No," replied Ekwefi. "His shell broke into pieces. But there was a great medicine man in the neighborhood. Tortoise's wife sent for him and he gathered all the bits of shell and stuck them together. That is why Tortoise's shell is not smooth."

TAKE NOTES

Literary Analysis

Personification sometimes shows human behavior in a funny way. What human behavior is the author showing in a funny way in this story?

_____

_____

Vocabulary and Pronunciation

Regular verbs in English usually end in *-ed* in the past tense. For example, *stopped* is the past tense of *stop*. Circle all the past tense verbs with the *-ed* ending on this page.

Stop to Reflect

Do you think Tortoise learned his lesson? Explain.

_____

_____

_____

Reading Skill

Recall the **purpose** you **set** at the beginning of the story. Restate your purpose here. Did you achieve your purpose while reading? Explain.

_____

_____

Vocabulary Development

machetes (ma SHET eez) *n.*   large heavy-bladed knives

Why the Tortoise's Shell Is Not Smooth

1. **Analyze:** The birds are not going to help Tortoise at first. Why do the birds decide to help Tortoise go to the feast?

   _____

   _____

2. **Interpret:** Tortoise tells the birds to call him by a new name. Explain how Tortoise's new name allows him to eat before the birds eat.

   _____

   _____

3. **Reading Skill:** Your **purpose** for reading is the reason you read a text. What would your purpose be for reading a nonfiction article about tortoises?

   _____

4. **Literary Analysis: Personification** gives human qualities to nonhuman subjects. Use the chart below to analyze the personification of Tortoise. First, list the ways in which Tortoise behaves like an animal. Then, list the ways in which Tortoise behaves like a human.

Character's Name: Tortoise	
Animal Qualities:	**Human Qualities:**

SUPPORT FOR WRITING AND EXTEND YOUR LEARNING

Writing: Invitation

Write an **invitation** to the birds' feast in the sky. Use the following questions to help you include details in your invitation.

- What is unusual about the feast?

  _____

- How should guests dress for the feast?

  _____

- What is the reason for such a feast?

  _____

Research and Technology: Presentation

Create a **presentation** of two folk tales with different origins. Use this chart to help you organize information for your presentation. Fill in the information as you read each folk tale.

Folk Tales from Different Countries	
Folk Tale #1	**Folk Tale #2:**
Country	Country
Purpose	Purpose
What tale is about	What tale is about
Characters	Characters
Lesson	Lesson

Editorials

ABOUT EDITORIALS

An **editorial** is a persuasive piece of writing that shares an editor's opinions on an issue. Editorials usually appear in newspapers, magazines, or other types of writing that are published regularly. Editorials have the following characteristics:

- They state an opinion that the editors or publishers think is important.
- They try to persuade readers to agree with that opinion.
- They use facts and reasons to support the opinion.

READING SKILL

You can **adjust your reading rate** to your **purpose for reading**.

- **Skim**, or glance quickly through a work. Skim to get a general idea of what the work is about.
- **Scan**, or quickly read through a work. Scan to find specific information, key words or ideas, or answers to a question.

Use this chart to help you skim and scan for different purposes.

To determine overall topic and source of text	**Skim** title, first paragraph, and source of information
To answer questions about when something happened	**Scan** for mention of days, months, or years
To answer questions about a specific term	**Scan** for the term or related key words in the question
To answer questions about a person or group	**Scan** for the name of the person or group

---

Build Understanding

Knowing these words will help you read this editorial.

commendable (kuh MEND uh buhl) *adj.* deserving of recommendation or praise

frill (fril) *n.* luxury

PORTSMOUTH HERALD

Music for ALL

Traip music students' effort is commendable

And the band played on.

This past Tuesday night, Traip Academy students were eloquent when asking the School Committee not to bring the curtain down on the town's music program.

First, the students noted, a good high school education should go beyond reading, writing and arithmetic. We all learn differently and for some, music will be the pied piper leading them on a path to higher learning[1]. The students also noted that the band is more than an academic endeavor, it is a part of town life that everyone can enjoy. Finally, the students pointed out that teenagers who are busy rehearsing and playing music are not out getting into trouble.

Clearly, the Kittery School Committee heard the message of these commendable students and decided to discuss the matter in greater detail at a public meeting on Feb. 26 with the goal of finding some other way to hold the line on education spending in town.

We understand that the Town Council does not have an endless pot of gold and cannot fund everything at the levels residents might desire. When money gets tight, tough choices have to be made.

But we would encourage the School Committee to look at the music program as essential, in many ways just as important as math, science and literature. Cuts to the program should be viewed with the same horror as we would view cuts to core curriculum.

Music is not a frill. It is one of mankind's greatest accomplishments and, at times, it can teach and inspire in a way that words and equations cannot.

We hope 2004 will not be the year the music dies in Kittery.

---

1. pied piper . . . learning an **allusion** to the folk tale about a musician who leads a town's children away.

THINKING ABOUT THE EDITORIAL

1. Would this article be useful to a reader whose purpose is to form an opinion on the value of music programs in schools? Explain.

_____

_____

2. Explain how a school music program can benefit a town.

_____

_____

READING SKILL

3. **Skim** the text. What is the overall topic of the editorial?

_____

4. **Scan** the text for the editorial opinion about the music program at Traip Academy.

_____

_____

TIMED WRITING: PERSUASION (20 minutes)

Write a letter to the School Committee. Persuade the committee to keep or cut the music program.

- Decide whether you want to keep or cut the music program. Write a sentence or two explaining why you think as you do.
- Read through the editorial. Underline any information that supports your opinion. Refer to the underlined material as you write.
- Write your opinion in the form of a letter.

The Stone • The Three Wishes

READING SKILL

Setting a purpose for reading can help you focus as you read. One purpose you may set is to **make connections**. You can make connections between your own life and what you are reading.

Here are three ways to make connections.

- Look for universal themes.

- Look for details that tell you about different cultures.

- Look for ideas in the text that might apply to your own life.

LITERARY ANALYSIS

The theme of a literary work is the basic idea it has about life. A **universal theme** is an idea about life that has been explained many times in many different cultures. Examples of universal themes include the importance of courage, the power of love, and the danger of greed.

Look for a universal theme by focusing on the story's main character, the problems that the character has, changes the character experiences, and the effects of the changes that the character experiences.

Use this chart to help you determine the universal theme as you read.

Character	
How character changes	
Meaning of change	
Universal theme	

The Stone

Lloyd Alexander

Summary Maibon is worried about getting old. He helps a dwarf in exchange for a wish. Maibon asks for a stone that will stop him from growing old. The dwarf tries to warn Maibon about such a stone. Things turn out differently than Maibon expects.

Reading/Writing Connection

Complete this paragraph to describe how three wishes might change a life.

A person would want to <u>acquire</u> _____. He

or she might use another wish to <u>obtain</u> _____.

These things would <u>enable</u> the person to _____.

Note-taking Guide

Events cause results in stories. Events from "The Stone" are listed in the left column of the chart. Record details about the results of these events.

Event	Result
Maibon helps the dwarf.	The dwarf rewards him with a wish.
The dwarf gives Maibon a stone that will stop him from growing old.	
Maibon gets rid of the stone.	

The Stone

1. **Infer:** Why does Maibon choose the stone over all of the other gifts?

   _____

   _____

   _____

2. **Analyze:** Maibon finally gets rid of the stone at the end of the story. What new belief allows him to give up the stone?

   _____

   _____

   _____

3. **Reading Skill:** Readers can **make connections** between their lives and what they are reading. Use this chart to note how details in the story helped you achieve the **purpose** of making connections.

Universal Theme	Cultural Details	Connections to Life
It is important to let life take its natural course.		

4. **Literary Analysis:** A **universal theme** is a lesson about life. Doli explains to Mabion why the stone will not go away. What universal theme is shown in the story after this scene?

   _____

   _____

   _____

SUPPORT FOR WRITING AND EXTEND YOUR LEARNING

Writing: Plot Proposal

Write a **plot proposal**, or plan of story events, that illustrates a universal theme from "The Stone." First, write a sentence that describes the story's theme.

_____

_____

Then, invent a new plot that contains the same theme. Use this chart to organize your notes for your proposal.

	What happens?	How does what happens relate to the story's theme?
Beginning of plot		
Middle of plot		
End of plot		

Research and Technology: Report

Write a **report** on human growth. Use the chart to record information about what happens to various parts of the body as humans age.

Characteristics	Description of characteristic in younger people	Description of characteristic in elderly people
Cells		
Skin		
Organs (such as the heart or the brain)		
Abilities (such as hearing or eyesight)		

The Three Wishes

Ricardo E. Alegría

Summary A woodsman and his wife live together in the forest. They are poor but happy. One day a stranger gives the wife three wishes. The wishes cause problems for the couple. The woodsman and his wife discover that happiness comes from love and not from riches.

Reading/Writing Connection

Complete these sentences to describe what can happen when you wish for something.

1. Wishing for something might help you <u>acquire</u> _____.

2. If the wish <u>exceeds</u> what you had hoped, you might feel

_____.

3. Do not <u>presume</u> that _____.

Note-taking Guide

Use this chart to record what happens when the characters use each wish.

Wish	Result
The wife accidentally wishes that her husband were with her.	The husband appears in the house.

The Three Wishes
Ricardo E. Alegría

Long ago a woodsman and his wife lived in a small house in the forest. They were poor but happy. And they always shared what they had with others. One day while the husband was working far away in the forest, an old man came to the house. He was lost and hungry. The wife gave him something to eat. After he ate, the old man said he would reward her for her kindness.

◆   ◆   ◆

The old man answered, "Beginning immediately, any three wishes you or your husband may wish will come true."

When she heard these words, the woman was <u>overjoyed</u> and exclaimed, "Oh, if my husband were only here to hear what you say!"

The last words had scarcely left her lips when the woodsman appeared in the little house with the ax still in his hands. The first wish had come true.

◆   ◆   ◆

His wife hugged him happily and told him what had happened. The husband, without thinking, became angry with his wife for wasting one of the wishes. He had never been angry with her before. His greed made him yell at her. He told her she was stupid and wished that she would grow donkey ears. And she did.

When she felt her ears, she began to cry. Her husband was sorry and ran to comfort her.

◆   ◆   ◆

TAKE NOTES

Activate Prior Knowledge

Think about another story in which a strange visitor gives wishes to the characters in the story. Name or describe the story.

_____

_____

Literary Analysis

One way to look for a **universal theme** is to focus on the problems that the characters in a story face. What problem do the woodsman and his wife have at the beginning of the story?

_____

Reading Skill

Making connections between a story and your life can help you focus as you read. Which details in the story relate to your life?

_____

_____

Reading Check

Where do the woodsman and his wife live? Underline the answer in the text.

Vocabulary Development

overjoyed (oh ver JOYD) *adj.*   extremely happy

"Quarreled" is a verb in English that means, "fought." It is pronounced, "KWAR ruhld." Many other words in English that begin with the letters *qu-* sound like they begin with *kw*. Some other examples are *quick*, *quarter*, and *question*.

Read Fluently

Nouns can be people, places, things, or ideas. An idea is an *abstract noun* because you cannot see, smell, hear, taste, or feel it. Put a star above two abstract nouns in the bracketed passage.

Stop to Reflect

Do you think the woodsman and his wife make a good third wish? Explain.

_____

_____

_____

Reading Check

What does the couple receive at the end of the story? Circle the sentence that tells you the answer.

The old man, who had stood by silently, now came to them and said, "Until now, you have known happiness together and have never quarreled with each other. Nevertheless, the mere knowledge that you could have riches and power has changed you both. Remember, you have only one wish left. What do you want? Riches? Beautiful clothes? Servants? Power?"

The woodsman tightened his arm about his wife, looked at the man, and said, "We want only the happiness and joy we knew before my wife grew donkey's ears."

◆ ◆ ◆

As soon as the husband spoke, his wife's ears were fixed. They hugged each other and gave thanks for their happiness. The old man told them that poor people can be happy, just as rich people can be unhappy. As a reward for their last wish, the old man made them as happy as they could be. A son was born to them. They all lived happily ever after.

Vocabulary Development

mere (meer) *adj.* simple; basic

The Three Wishes

1. **Compare and Contrast:** The chance to make wishes can change people. How does the couple's behavior change?

   _____

   _____

   _____

2. **Interpret:** How does the saying "Be careful what you wish for" apply to the couple?

   _____

   _____

3. **Reading Skill:** A **purpose** can help you focus as you read. Use this chart to note how details in the story helped you achieve the purpose of making connections.

Universal Theme	Cultural Details	Connections to Life
People often wish for things that may not bring happiness when the people obtain them.		

4. **Literary Analysis:** Read the first paragraph of the story. What **universal theme**, or message about life, does the couple's kindness and willingness to share suggest?

   _____

   _____

SUPPORT FOR WRITING AND EXTEND YOUR LEARNING

Writing: Plot Proposal

Write a **plot proposal**, or plan of story events, that illustrates the universal theme from "The Three Wishes." First, write a sentence that describes the story's theme.

_____

_____

Then, invent a new plot that contains the same theme. Use this chart to organize your notes for your proposal.

	What happens?	How does what happens relate to the story's theme?
Beginning of plot		
Middle of plot		
End of plot		

Listening and Speaking: Oral Response

Present an **oral response** to the theme of "The Three Wishes." First, write a sentence that describes the story's theme.

_____

_____

Then, use this chart to help you organize your response.

	Description	How does the example relate to the story's theme?	Does the example show that you agree or disagree with the story's theme?
Example from another story			
Example from your own life			

Practice your response before you present it.

PART 2: TURBO VOCABULARY

The exercises and tools presented here are designed to help you increase your vocabulary. Review the instruction and complete the exercises to build your vocabulary knowledge. Throughout the year, you can apply these skills and strategies to improve your reading, writing, speaking, and listening vocabulary.

The following list contains common word roots with meanings and examples. On the blank lines, write other words you know that have the same roots. Write the meanings of the new words.

Root	Meaning	Example and Meaning	Your Words	Meanings
-brev-	brief; short	*brevity:* the quality of lasting for a short time		
-dict-	say or tell	*predict:* tell what might happen next		
-fer-	bring; carry	*reference:* something you say or write that mentions another person or thing, something that brings or carries more information		
-port-	carry	*support:* carry or hold something up		

Root	Meaning	Example and Meaning	Your Words	Meanings
-scrib-	write	*scribble:* write something quickly in a messy way		
-spec-	look; see	*inspect:* look carefully at something		
-ver-	truth	*verify:* make sure something is true		

PREFIXES

The following list contains common prefixes with meanings and examples. On the blank lines, write other words you know that begin with the same prefixes. Write the meanings of the new words.

Prefix	Meaning	Example and Meaning	Your Words	Meanings
con-	with; together	*concur:* agree with		
de-	down; from	*decrease:* become less		
dis-	not	*disorganized:* not organized		
in-	without; not	*incapable:* not able		

Prefix	Meaning	Example and Meaning	Your Words	Meanings
non-	without; not	*nonfat:* without fat		
pre-	before	*preview:* look before		
re-	again	*remake:* make again		
un-/an-/a-	not	*unbelievable:* not believable		

SUFFIXES

The following list contains common suffixes with meanings and examples. On the blank lines, write other words you know that have the same suffixes. Write the meanings of the new words.

Suffix	Meaning	Example and Meaning	Your Words	Meanings
-able/-ible	able to be	*movable:* able to be moved		
-er/-or	one who	*actor:* person who acts		
-ful	filled with	*joyful:* filled with happiness		
-ish	resembling	*foolish:* not sensible		

Suffix	Meaning	Example and Meaning	Your Words	Meanings
-ist	one who	*violinist:* person who plays the violin		
-less	without	*powerless:* without power		
-ly	in a way	*quickly:* done in a short amount of time		
-ment	act or quality of	*excitement:* feeling of being excited		
-ness	state or quality of	*kindness:* friendly and caring behavior		
-sion/-tion	act or process of	*persuasion:* act of convincing someone		

Use a **dictionary** to find the correct spelling, the meaning, the pronunciation, and the part of speech of a word. The dictionary will show you how the plural is formed if it is irregular. You can also find the word's history, or *etymology*, in a dictionary. Etymology explains how words change, how they are borrowed from other languages, and how new words are invented, or "coined."

Here is a sample entry from a dictionary. Notice what it tells about the word. Then, follow the instructions.

lemon (lem´ ən) *n.* [ME *lymon* < MFr *limon* < Ar *laimūn* < Pers *līmūn*] **1** a small, egg-shaped, edible citrus fruit with a yellow rind and a juicy, sour pulp, rich in ascorbic acid **2** the small, spiny, semitropical evergreen citrus tree (*Citrus limon*) bearing this fruit **3** pale yellow **4** [slang] something, esp. a manufactured article, that is defective or imperfect

1. Circle the *n.* in the dictionary entry. It stands for noun. Write what these other parts of speech abbreviations mean: *v.* _____, *adv.* _____, *adj.* _____ *prep.* _____.

2. Underline the origins of the word *lemon.* ME stands for Middle English, Ar stands for Arabic, and Pers. stands for Persian. What do you think MFr stands for? _____

3. Put a box around the pronunciation.

4. How many noun definitions does the entry have? _____

5. Which definition is slang? _____

6. Which definition of lemon is used in the following sentence? _____

The car that my dad bought turned out to be a lemon.

Activity: Use a dictionary to learn about the origins of these words.

1. literature _____ / _____ / _____
              pronunciation   main part of speech   original language(s)

_____ / _____
      1st meaning   other meanings

_____

_____

_____

_____

2. language _____ / _____ / _____
              pronunciation   main part of speech   original language(s)

_____ / _____
      1st meaning   other meanings

_____

_____

_____

Activity: Look up each of the following words in a dictionary. Then, write a definition of the word and a sentence using the word.

moment _____

_____

popular _____

_____

remedy _____

_____

blur _____

_____

lazy _____

_____

WORD STUDY CARDS

Use these word study cards to break big words into their parts. Write the word at the top of the card. Then, divide the word into its prefix, root, and suffix. Note that not all words have prefixes and suffixes. List the meaning of each part of the word. Next, find three words with the same root and write them on the card. Finally, write the word's part of speech and its definition. Use a dictionary to help you. One example has been done for you.

Word:	invisible	
Prefix	**Root**	**Suffix**
in: not	**vis:** see	**ible**-able to be

Root-related Words
1. vision
2. revise
3. visibility

Definition: invisible *adj.* not able to be seen

Word:		
Prefix	**Root**	**Suffix**

Root-related Words
1.
2.
3.

Definition:

Word:

Prefix	Root	Suffix

Root-related Words
1.
2.
3.

Definition:

Word:

Prefix	Root	Suffix

Root-related Words
1.
2.
3.

Definition:

Word:

Prefix	Root	Suffix

Root-related Words
1.
2.
3.

Definition:

fact (FAKT) *n.* a statement that can be proved

It is a *fact* that George Washington was the first president of the United States.

opinion (uh PIN yuhn) *n.* a statement that expresses a person's judgment or belief

In my *opinion*, North Carolina is a good place to live.

predict (pree DIKT) *v.* make a logical assumption about what will happen next

I *predict* that the characters will be trapped by the storm.

prove (PROOV) *v.* show evidence

Prove that water contains oxygen and hydrogen.

support (suh POHRT) *v.* uphold; offer proof

I *support* my prediction with my knowledge about storms.

A. Completion Complete each sentence that has been started for you. Your sentence completion should be logical and illustrate the meaning of the vocabulary word in italics.

1. You put *facts* into a report in order to _____

_____

2. In my *opinion*, it is better to be _____

_____

3. By experimenting, the scientist was able to *prove* _____

_____

4. I can *predict* what will happen tomorrow by _____

_____

5. The journalist was able to *support* his story with

_____

B. Use each word pair in an original sentence that illustrates the meaning of the academic vocabulary word.

fact/research _____

_____

opinion/conversation _____

_____

predict/outcome _____

_____

prove/theory _____

_____

support/examples _____

_____

C. Write new words that you come across in your reading. Define each word.

_____

_____

_____

_____

_____

conclude (kuhn KLOOD) *v.* form an opinion or make a judgment, based on evidence presented

Based on what I know about monkeys, I *conclude* that the character will succeed.

detail (di TAYL) *n.* a piece of information

The *details* in the story act as clues for the reader.

examine (eg ZAM uhn) *v.* look at carefully

Examine the character's motives.

infer (in FER) *v.* assume something based on facts

You can *infer* from the music that something scary is going to happen.

speculate (SPEK yuh layt) *v.* make a prediction

We *speculate* that the main character will win the contest.

A. True/False For each of the following, mark T or F to indicate whether the italicized vocabulary word has been used correctly in the sentence. If you have marked F, correct the sentence by using the word properly.

1. _____ The *details* in the story act as clues for the reader.

   _____

2. _____ Based on the evidence, Molly was able to *conclude* that her friend was not guilty.

   _____

3. _____ Please, *speculate* the dishes after you are through eating.

   _____

4. _____ A doctor will *examine* you to find out if you are sick.

   _____

5. _____ Use the left blinker to *infer* that you are going to turn left.

   _____

B. Use each word pair in a sentence that shows the meaning of the academic vocabulary word.

conclude/essay _____

_____

detail/story _____

_____

examine/painting _____

_____

infer/information _____

_____

speculate/future _____

_____

C. Write new words that you come across in your reading. Define each word.

_____

_____

_____

_____

_____

determine (dee TER muhn) *v.* decide or figure out
Try to *determine* the author's key points.

identify (y DEN tuh fy) *v.* recognize or point out
I can *identify* a mistake that the author made.

influence (IN floo uhns) *n.* power to affect others
That book *influenced* many people.

intent (in TENT) *n.* purpose, objective, or aim
My *intent* was to finish my homework early.

significant (sig NIF uh kuhnt) *adj.* important
Every detail in the essay should be *significant*.

A. Code Name Use the code to figure out each vocabulary word. Each letter is represented by a number or symbol. This exercise will help you learn how to spell and recognize the vocabulary words.

%	5	•	*	2	#	!	7	^	&	9	¶	£	$	3	¥	+	=	?	÷	4	¢	6	§	«	ç
a	b	c	d	e	f	g	h	i	j	k	l	m	n	o	p	q	r	s	t	u	v	w	x	y	z

1. ^ $ ÷ 2 $ ÷   _____

2. * 2 ÷ 2 = £ ^ $ 2   _____

3. ^ $ # ¶ 4 2 $ • 2   _____

4. ? ^ ! $ ^ # ^ • % $ ÷   _____

5. ^ * 2 $ ÷ ^ # «   _____

B. Completion Complete each sentence that has been started for you. Your sentence should make sense and illustrate the meaning of the vocabulary word in italics.

1. Read the recipe to *determine* _____

_____.

2. To *identify* the part of speech of a word, you must _____

_____.

3. I have *influence* over _____.

_____.

4. My *intent* in going to school is _____

_____.

5. The most *significant* event of the day _____

_____.

C. Write new words that you come across in your reading. Define each word.

_____

_____

_____

_____

_____

context (KAHN tekst) *n.* situation in which a word is used
Figure out the definition from its *context*.

define (dee FYN) *v.* state the meaning
A dictionary will *define* that word.

explain (eks PLAYN) *v.* make clear or understandable
Can you *explain* the idea more simply?

paraphrase (PAR uh frayz) *v.* restate in your own words
Please *paraphrase* the quotation.

preview (PREE vyoo) *v.* view, or look at, beforehand
Preview to get an idea of the topic.

A. Unscramble each vocabulary word and write it on the line to the right. This exercise will help you learn how to spell and recognize the vocabulary words.

1. w e e r p i v   _____

2. t o c x n e t   _____

3. r a s h a p e r p a   _____

4. e d e n i f   _____

5. p a x e l n i   _____

B. True/False For each of the following, mark T or F to indicate whether the italicized vocabulary word has been used correctly in the sentence. If you have marked F, correct the sentence by changing the words that make the sentence wrong.

1. _____ You can figure out how to spell a word by looking at its *context*.

_____

2. _____ If you want to *define* a new word, use an almanac.

_____

3. _____ Joe will *explain* the situation clearly, so that Martha will be able to understand.

_____

4. _____ If you *paraphrase* what an author has written, you copy it word for word.

_____

5. _____ It is a good idea for the parents to *preview* a movie before letting young children see it.

_____

C. Write new words that you come across in your reading. Define each word.

_____

_____

_____

_____

compare (kuhm PAYR) *v.* show how things are alike
Compare the plays in an essay.

contrast (kuhn TRAST) *v.* show how things are different
Contrast the character's motives.

describe (di SKRYB) *v.* tell or write about
Describe the details of the scene.

review (ri VYOO) *v.* look at again
Review your work for errors.

summary (SUM uh ree) *n.* the main ideas in brief form
Write a *summary* of the story.

A. True/False For each of the following, mark T or F to indicate whether the italicized vocabulary word has been used correctly in the sentence. If you have marked F, correct the sentence by changing the words that make the sentence wrong.

1. _____ Paul wrote a *summary* of the book before he began the first chapter.

2. _____ Julia *described* her summer vacation in vivid detail.

3. _____ Jacob was planning to *review* his essay before he began writing it.

4. _____ Neill showed how both objects were alike by *contrasting* their similar traits.

5. _____ When you *compare* two houses, you should discuss how they are alike.

B. Completion Complete each sentence that has been started for you. Your sentence completion should be logical and illustrate the meaning of the vocabulary word in italics.

1. We *compared* the movie to the book to see if _____

_____.

2. We couldn't wait to see the movie after Ralph *described* _____

_____.

3. After Julia *summarized* the story, I _____

_____.

4. There is a great *contrast* between _____

_____.

5. It is important to *review* your homework in order to _____

_____.

C. Write new words that you come across in your reading. Define each word.

_____

_____

_____

_____

cause (KAWZ) *n.* the reason something happens

Heavy rain was the *cause* of the flood.

effect (e FEKT) *n.* the consequence of

The *effect* of practice is that you become a better writer.

establish (uh STAB lish) *v.* set up; cause to be

To help *establish* a purpose for reading, you preview the text.

relationship (ri LAY shuhn ship) *n.* the connection between two things

The connection between a cause and its effect is their *relationship*.

purpose (PER puhs) *n.* intent; plan

When you read with a *purpose*, you read more effectively.

A. Code Name Use the code to figure out each vocabulary word. Each letter is represented by a number or symbol. This exercise will help you learn how to spell and recognize the vocabulary words.

%	5	•	*	2	#	!	7	^	&	9	¶	£	$	3	¥	+	=	?	÷	4	¢	6	§	«	ç
a	b	c	d	e	f	g	h	i	j	k	l	m	n	o	p	q	r	s	t	u	v	w	x	y	z

1. 2 ? ÷ % 5 ¶ ^ ? 7   _____

2. ¥ 4 = ¥ 3 ? 2   _____

3. = 2 ¶ % ÷ ^ 3 $? 7 ^ ¥   _____

4. • % 4 ? 2   _____

5. 2 # # 2 • ÷   _____

B. True/False For each of the following, mark T or F to indicate whether the italicized vocabulary word has been used correctly in the sentence. If you have marked F, correct the sentence by using the word properly.

1. _____ An emergency shelter was *established* before the hurricane.

   _____

2. _____ The *cause* of the flood was the dam bursting.

   _____

3. _____ The principal and teachers have a good *relationship*.

   _____

4. _____ The *effect* of passing a test is studying very hard.

   _____

5. _____ A common *purpose* for reading a textbook is to be entertained.

   _____

C. Write new words that you come across in your reading. Define each word.

_____

_____

_____

_____

_____

_____

_____

_____

_____

Use this page to write down academic words you come across in other subjects, such as social studies or science. When you are reading your textbooks, you may find words that you need to learn. Following the example, write down the word, the part of speech, and an explanation of the word. You may want to write an example sentence to help you remember the word.

dissolve *verb* to make something solid become part of a liquid by putting it in a liquid and mixing it

The sugar *dissolved* in the hot tea.

_____

_____

_____

_____

_____

_____

_____

_____

_____

_____

_____

_____

_____

_____

_____

_____

_____

_____

_____

_____

Use these flash cards to study words you want to remember. The words on this page come from Unit 1. Cut along the dotted lines on pages V25 through V32 to create your own flash cards or use index cards. Write the word on the front of the card. On the back, write the word's part of speech and definition. Then, write a sentence that shows the meaning of the word.

grief	reflection	abruptly
prelude	evident	winced
timidly	grudgingly	ignore

noun
deep sadness

When he husband died, her *grief* was obvious.

---

noun
an image of one's self, as seen in a mirror

I saw a *reflection* of my face in the windowpane.

---

adverb
suddenly, without warning

The bus stopped so *abruptly*, I fell off my seat

---

noun
introduction to a main event

We sang the school song as a *prelude* to the big game.

---

adjective
easy to see; very clear

Her happiness was *evident* in her cheery smile.

---

verb
drew back slightly, as if in pain; cringed

The boy *winced* as the nurse gave him a shot.

---

adverb
in a way that shows fear or shyness

Frightened, Rosa *timidly* asked a question.

---

adverb
in an unwilling or resentful way

Max *grudgingly* admitted his mistake.

---

verb
pay no attention to

Anna tried to *ignore* the car alarm.

Use these flash cards to study words you want to remember. Cut along the dotted lines on pages V25 through V32 to create your own flash cards or use index cards. Write the word on the front of the card. On the back, write the word's part of speech and definition. Then, write a sentence that shows the meaning of the word.

Use these flash cards to study words you want to remember. Cut along the dotted lines on pages V25 through V32 to create your own flash cards or use index cards. Write the word on the front of the card. On the back, write the word's part of speech and definition. Then, write a sentence that shows the meaning of the word.

Use these flash cards to study words you want to remember. Cut along the dotted lines on pages V25 through V32 to create your own flash cards or use index cards. Write the word on the front of the card. On the back, write the word's part of speech and definition. Then, write a sentence that shows the meaning of the word.

VOCABULARY FOLD-A-LIST

Use a fold-a-list to study the definitions of words. The words on this page come from Unit 1. Write the definition for each word on the lines. Fold the paper along the dotted line to check your definition. Create your own fold-a-lists on pages V35 through V38.

sympathy   _____

                _____

compulsion   _____

                _____

intently   _____

                _____

awed   _____

                _____

mode   _____

                _____

frenzied   _____

                _____

inhabited   _____

                _____

seized   _____

                _____

suspended   _____

                _____

revelation   _____

                _____

Fold In ←

VOCABULARY FOLD-A-LIST

Write the word that matches the definition on each line.
Fold the paper along the dotted line to check your work.

shared feeling _____

driving force _____

purposefully; earnestly _____

filled with feelings
of fear and wonder _____

way of doing something _____

acting in a wild,
uncontrolled way _____

lived in; occupied _____

grabbed; taken hold of _____

stopped for a time _____

sudden rush
of understanding _____

Fold In ←

VOCABULARY FOLD-A-LIST

Write the words you want to study on this side of the page. Write the definitions on the back. Then, test yourself. Fold the paper along the dotted line to check your answers.

Word: _____

_____

Word: _____

_____

Word: _____

_____

Word: _____

_____

Word: _____

_____

Word: _____

_____

Word: _____

_____

Word: _____

_____

Word: _____

_____

Word: _____

_____

Fold In ←

VOCABULARY FOLD-A-LIST

Write the word that matches the definition on each line.
Fold the paper along the dotted line to check your work.

Definition: _____

_____

Definition: _____

_____

Definition: _____

_____

Definition: _____

_____

Definition: _____

_____

Definition: _____

_____

Definition: _____

_____

Definition: _____

Definition: _____

_____

Definition: _____

_____

Fold In ◄

VOCABULARY FOLD-A-LIST

Write the words you want to study on this side of the page. Write the definitions on the back. Then, test yourself. Fold the paper along the dotted line to check your answers.

Word: _____

_____

Word: _____

_____

Word: _____

_____

Word: _____

_____

Word: _____

_____

Word: _____

_____

Word: _____

_____

Word: _____

_____

Word: _____

_____

Word: _____

_____

Word: _____

_____

Fold In ◄

VOCABULARY FOLD-A-LIST

Write the word that matches the definition on each line.
Fold the paper along the dotted line to check your work.

Definition: _____

_____

Definition: _____

_____

Definition: _____

_____

Definition: _____

_____

Definition: _____

_____

Definition: _____

_____

Definition: _____

_____

Definition: _____

Definition: _____

_____

Definition: _____

_____

Fold In ←

The list on these pages presents words that cause problems for many people. Some of these words are spelled according to set rules, but others follow no specific rules. As you review this list, check to see how many of the words give you trouble in your own writing. Then, add your own commonly misspelled words on the lines that follow.

abbreviate	auxiliary	census	deficient
absence	awkward	certain	definitely
absolutely	bandage	changeable	delinquent
abundance	banquet	characteristic	dependent
accelerate	bargain	chauffeur	descendant
accidentally	barrel	chief	description
accumulate	battery	clothes	desert
accurate	beautiful	coincidence	desirable
ache	beggar	colonel	dessert
achievement	beginning	column	deteriorate
acquaintance	behavior	commercial	dining
adequate	believe	commission	disappointed
admittance	benefit	commitment	disastrous
advertisement	bicycle	committee	discipline
aerial	biscuit	competitor	dissatisfied
affect	bookkeeper	concede	distinguish
aggravate	bought	condemn	effect
aggressive	boulevard	congratulate	eighth
agreeable	brief	connoisseur	eligible
aisle	brilliant	conscience	embarrass
all right	bruise	conscientious	enthusiastic
allowance	bulletin	conscious	entrepreneur
aluminum	buoyant	contemporary	envelope
amateur	bureau	continuous	environment
analysis	bury	controversy	equipped
analyze	buses	convenience	equivalent
ancient	business	coolly	especially
anecdote	cafeteria	cooperate	exaggerate
anniversary	calendar	cordially	exceed
anonymous	campaign	correspondence	excellent
answer	canceled	counterfeit	exercise
anticipate	candidate	courageous	exhibition
anxiety	capacity	courteous	existence
apologize	capital	courtesy	experience
appall	capitol	criticism	explanation
appearance	captain	criticize	extension
appreciate	career	curiosity	extraordinary
appropriate	carriage	curious	familiar
architecture	cashier	cylinder	fascinating
argument	catastrophe	deceive	February
associate	category	decision	fiery
athletic	ceiling	deductible	financial
attendance	cemetery	defendant	fluorescent

foreign
fourth
fragile
gauge
generally
genius
genuine
government
grammar
grievance
guarantee
guard
guidance
handkerchief
harass
height
humorous
hygiene
ignorant
immediately
immigrant
independence
independent
indispensable
individual
inflammable
intelligence
interfere
irrelevant
irritable
jewelry
judgment
knowledge
lawyer
legible
legislature
leisure
liable
library
license
lieutenant
lightning
likable
liquefy
literature
loneliness
magnificent
maintenance
marriage
mathematics
maximum
meanness
mediocre
mileage
millionaire
minimum

minuscule
miscellaneous
mischievous
misspell
mortgage
naturally
necessary
neighbor
neutral
nickel
niece
ninety
noticeable
nuisance
obstacle
occasion
occasionally
occur
occurred
occurrence
omitted
opinion
opportunity
optimistic
outrageous
pamphlet
parallel
paralyze
parentheses
particularly
patience
permanent
permissible
perseverance
persistent
personally
perspiration
persuade
phenomenal
phenomenon
physician
pleasant
pneumonia
possess
possession
possibility
prairie
precede
preferable
prejudice
preparation
previous
primitive
privilege
probably
procedure

proceed
prominent
pronunciation
psychology
publicly
pursue
questionnaire
realize
really
recede
receipt
receive
recognize
recommend
reference
referred
rehearse
relevant
reminiscence
renowned
repetition
restaurant
rhythm
ridiculous
sandwich
satellite
schedule
scissors
secretary
siege
solely
sponsor
subtle
subtlety
superintendent
supersede
surveillance
susceptible
tariff
temperamental
theater
threshold
truly
unmanageable
unwieldy
usage
usually
valuable
various
vegetable
voluntary
weight
weird
whale
wield
yield

_____

_____

_____

_____

_____

_____

_____

_____

_____

_____

_____

_____

_____

_____

_____

_____

_____

_____

When you are reading, you will find many unfamiliar words. Here are some tools that you can use to help you read unfamiliar words.

PHONICS

Phonics is the science or study of sound. When you learn to read, you learn to associate certain sounds with certain letters or letter combinations. You know most of the sounds that letters can represent in English. When letters are combined, however, it is not always so easy to know what sound is represented. In English, there are some rules and patterns that will help you determine how to pronounce a word. This chart shows you some of the vowel digraphs, which are combinations like *ea* and *oa*. Two vowels together are called vowel digraphs. Usually, vowel digraphs represent the long sound of the first vowel.

Vowel Digraphs	Examples of Unusual Sounds	Exceptions
ee and *ea*	steep, each, treat, sea	head, sweat, dread
ai and *ay*	plain, paid, may, betray	
oa, *ow*, and *oe*	soak, slow, doe	rot, box
ie, *igh*, and *y*	lie, night, my, delight	with, lit, myth

As you read, sometimes the only way to know how to pronounce a word with an *ea* spelling is to see if the word makes sense in the sentence. Look at this example:

The water pipes were made of *lead*.

First, try out the long sound "ee." Ask yourself if it sounds right. It does not. Then, try the short sound "e." You will find that the short sound is correct in that sentence.

Now try this example.

Where you *lead*, I will follow.

WORD PATTERNS

Recognizing different vowel-consonant patterns will help you read longer words. In the following sections, the V stands for "vowel" and the C stands for "consonant."

Single-syllable Words

CV – go: In two letter words with a consonant followed by a vowel, the vowel is usually long. For example, the word *go* is pronounced with a long *o* sound.

In a single syllable word, a vowel followed only by a single consonant is usually short.

CVC – got: If you add a consonant to the word *go*, such as the *t* in *got*, the vowel sound is a short *o*. Say the words *go* and *got* aloud and notice the difference in pronunciation.

Multi-syllable words

In words of more than one syllable, notice the letters that follow a vowel.

VCCV – robber: A single vowel followed by two consonants is usually short

VCV — begin: a single vowel followed by a single consonant is usually long.

VCe — beside: An extension of the VCV pattern is vowel-consonant-silent *e*. In these words, the vowel is long and the *e* is not pronounced.

When you see a word with the VCV pattern, try the long vowel sound first. If the word does not make sense, try the short sound. Pronounce the words *model*, *camel*, and *closet*. First, try the long vowel sound. That does not sound correct, so try the short vowel sound. The short vowel sound is correct in those words.

Remember that patterns help you get started on figuring out a word. You will sometimes need to try a different sound or find the word in a dictionary.

As you read and find unfamiliar words, look the pronunciations up in a dictionary. Write the words in this chart in the correct column, to help you notice patterns and remember pronunciations.

Syllables	Example	New words	Vowel
CV	go		long
CVC	got		short
VCC	robber		short
V/CV	begin open		long long
VC/V	Closet		short

MNEMONICS

Mnemonics are devices, or methods, that help you remember things. The basic strategy is to link something you do not know with something that you *do* know. Here are some common mnemonic devices:

Visualizing Create a picture in your head that will help you remember the meaning of a vocabulary word. For example, the first four letters of the word *significance* spell *sign.* Picture a sign with the word *meaning* written on it to remember that significance means "meaning" or "importance."

Spelling The way a word is spelled can help you remember its meaning. For example, you might remember that *clarify* means to "make clear" if you notice that both *clarify* and *clear* start with the letters *cl.*

To help you remember how to spell certain words, look for a familiar word within the difficult word. For example:

Believe has a *lie* in it.

Separate is *a rat* of a word to spell.

Your *principal* is your *pal.*

Rhyming Here is a popular rhyme that helps people figure out how to spell *ei* and *ie* words.

i before *e* — except after *c* or *when sounding like* *a* *as in neighbor and weigh.*

List words here that you need help remembering. Work with a group to create mnemonic devices to help you remember each word.

_____   _____

_____   _____

_____   _____

_____   _____

_____   _____

List words here that you need help remembering. Work with a group to create mnemonic devices to help you remember each word.

_____   _____

_____   _____

_____   _____

_____   _____

_____   _____

_____   _____

_____   _____

_____   _____

_____   _____

_____   _____

_____   _____

_____   _____

_____   _____

COMMUNICATION STRATEGIES

Use these sentence starters to help you express yourself clearly in different classroom situations.

Expressing an Opinion
I think that _____
I believe that _____
In my opinion, _____

Agreeing
I agree with _____ that _____
I see what you mean.
That's an interesting idea.
My idea is similar to _____'s idea.
My idea builds upon _____'s idea.

Disagreeing
I don't completely agree with you because _____
My opinion is different than yours.
I got a different answer than you.
I see it a different way.

Reporting a Group's Ideas
We agreed that _____
We decided that _____
We had a different approach.
We had a similar idea.

Predicting
I predict that _____
I imagine that _____
Based on _____ I predict that _____

Paraphrasing
So you are saying that _____
In other words, you think _____
What I hear you saying is _____

Offering a Suggestion
Maybe we could _____
What if we _____
Here's something we might try.

Asking for Clarification
I have a question about that.
Could you explain that another way?
Can you give me another example of that?

Asking for a Response
What do you think?
Do you agree?
What answer did you get?

IDIOMS

An **idiom** is a group of words that has a special meaning that is different from the ordinary meaning of each separate word. For example, to be *on top of the world* is an idiom that means to be "very happy." It does not mean to be physically on top of the world.

Every language is full of idioms. You can often find the definition of an idiom in a dictionary. Sometimes, you may have to ask a native speaker of the language to tell you what the idiom means. Keep a list of idioms and their definitions as you run across them in your reading.

A. Hypothesize Read each of the following sentences. Then, on the line below, write what you think the italicized idiom means.

1. I know you think I took your candy, but you are *barking up the wrong tree.*

_____

2. I would *give my right arm* to be able to go to Florida with my friend next month.

_____

3. Within an hour, the teacher had the noisy class *in hand.*

_____

4. Make sure you stay *on your toes* when you get to the city.

_____

5. I *could not believe my ears* when I heard I had won the contest.

_____

IDIOMS

As you read, you will find other idioms. Write them down in the chart. Write the idiom, an explanation of its meaning, and a sample sentence that shows it's use.

Idiom	Explanation	Sample Sentence
raining cats and dogs	raining very hard	We got very wet leaving the party because it was raining cats and dogs

VOCABULARY BOOKMARKS

Cut out each bookmark to use as a handy word list when you are reading. On the lines, jot down words you want to learn and remember. You can also use the bookmark as a placeholder in your book.

TITLE		TITLE		TITLE	
Word	**Page #**	**Word**	**Page #**	**Word**	**Page #**

VOCABULARY BOOKMARKS

Cut out each bookmark to use as a handy word list when you are reading. On the lines, jot down words you want to learn and remember. You can also use the bookmark as a placeholder in your book.

TITLE	
Word	Page #

TITLE	
Word	Page #

TITLE	
Word	Page #

VOCABULARY BUILDER CARDS

Use these cards to record words you want to remember. Write the word, the title of the story or article in which it appears, its part of speech, and its definition. Then, use the word in an original sentence that shows its meaning

Word: _____ Page _____

Selection: _____

Part of Speech: _____

Definition: _____

_____

My Sentence _____

_____

Word: _____ Page _____

Selection: _____

Part of Speech: _____

Definition: _____

_____

My Sentence _____

_____

Word: _____ Page _____

Selection: _____

Part of Speech: _____

Definition: _____

_____

My Sentence _____

_____

VOCABULARY BUILDER CARDS

Use these cards to record words you want to remember. Write the word, the title of the story or article in which it appears, its part of speech, and its definition. Then, use the word in an original sentence that shows its meaning

Word: _____ Page _____

Selection: _____

Part of Speech: _____

Definition: _____

My Sentence _____

_____

Word: _____ Page _____

Selection: _____

Part of Speech: _____

Definition: _____

My Sentence _____

_____

Word: _____ Page _____

Selection: _____

Part of Speech: _____

Definition: _____

My Sentence _____

_____

VOCABULARY BUILDER CARDS

Use these cards to record words you want to remember. Write the word, the title of the story or article in which it appears, its part of speech, and its definition. Then, use the word in an original sentence that shows its meaning

Word: _____ Page _____

Selection: _____

Part of Speech: _____

Definition: _____

_____

My Sentence _____

_____

Word: _____ Page _____

Selection: _____

Part of Speech: _____

Definition: _____

_____

My Sentence _____

_____

Word: _____ Page _____

Selection: _____

Part of Speech: _____

Definition: _____

_____

My Sentence _____

_____

VOCABULARY BUILDER CARDS

Use these cards to record words you want to remember. Write the word, the title of the story or article in which it appears, its part of speech, and its definition. Then, use the word in an original sentence that shows its meaning

Word: _____ Page _____

Selection: _____

Part of Speech: _____

Definition: _____

My Sentence _____

Word: _____ Page _____

Selection: _____

Part of Speech: _____

Definition: _____

My Sentence _____

Word: _____ Page _____

Selection: _____

Part of Speech: _____

Definition: _____

My Sentence _____

(Acknowledgments continued from page ii)

Samuel French, Inc.
"The Phantom Tollbooth A Children's Play In Two Acts" by Susan Nanus and Norton Juster. Copyright © 1977 by Susan Nanus and Norton Juster. All rights reserved. **CAUTION NOTICE:** Professionals and amateurs are hereby warned that *THE PHANTOM TOLLBOOTH A CHILDREN'S PLAY IN TWO ACTS* is subject to a royalty. It is fully protected under the copyright laws of the United States of America and of all countries covered by the International Copyright Union (including the Dominion of Canada and the rest of the British Commonwealth), the Berne Convention, the Pan-American Copyright Convention and the Universal Copyright Convention as well as all countries with which the United States has reciprocal copyright relations. All rights, including professional/amateur stage rights, motion picture, recitation, lecturing, public reading, radio broadcasting, television, video or sound recording, all other forms of mechanical or electronic reproduction, such as CD-ROM, CD-I, information storage and retrieval systems and photocopying, and the rights of translation into foreign languages, are strictly reserved. Particular emphasis is laid upon the matter of readings, permission for which must be secured from the Author's agent in writing.

Greenwillow Books
"Ankylosaurus" from *Tyrannosaurus Was A Beast* by Jack Prelutsky. Text copyright © 1988 by Jack Prelutsky. Reprinted by permission.

HarperCollins Publishers, Inc.
"No Thank You" by Shel Silverstein from *Falling Up*. Copyright © 1996 by Shel Silverstein. "The World is Not a Pleasant Place To Be" from *My House* by Nikki Giovanni. Copyright © 1972 by Nikki Giovanni. Reprinted by permission of Harper Collins Publishers, Inc. All rights reserved. "The Wounded Wolf" from *The Wounded Wolf* by Jean Craighead George. Text copyright © 1978 by Jean Craighead George.

Harper's Magazine
"Preserving the Great American Symbol" (originally titled "Descrating America") by Richard Durbin from *Harper's Magazine, October 1989, p.32*. Copyright © 1989 by Harper's Magazine. All rights reserved. Reproduced from the October issue by special permission.

Heinemann Educational Publishers
"Why the Tortoise's Shell Is Not Smooth" from *Things Fall Apart* by Chinua Achebe. Copyright © 1959 by Chinua Achebe.

The Barbara Hogenson Agency, Inc.
"The Tiger Who Would Be King" by James Thurber, from *Further Fables for Our Time*. Copyright © 1956 James Thurber. Copyright © renewed 1984 by Rosemary A. Thurber.

Houghton Mifflin Company
"Arachne" by Olivia Coolidge from *Greek Myths*. Copyright © 1949 by Olivia E. Coolidge; copyright renewed © 1977 by Olivia E. Coolidge. All rights reserved.

Dr. Francisco Jiménez
"The Circuit" by Francisco Jiménez from *America Street: A Mulicultural Anthology of Stories*. Copyright © 1993 by Anne Mazer.

Rachel Katz
"Origami with Rachel Katz: Apatosauras" by Katz Rachel from *www.geocities.com/rachel_katz*. Copyright © 2001–2004 Rachel Katz. All rights reserved. Reprinted by permission.

Alfred A. Knopf Children's Books
"Jackie Robinson: Justice at Last" from *25 Great Moments* by Geoffrey C. Ward and Ken Burns with S.A. Kramer, copyright © 1994 by Baseball Licensing International, Inc.

The Lazear Literary Agency
"Turkeys" from *Mama Makes Up Her Mind* (Addison-Wesley, 1993).

Madison County Public Library (Kentucky)
"Madison County Public Library Card Application Form" by Staff. From *Madison County Public Library*. Reprinted by permission.

Eve Merriam c/o Marian Reiner Literary Agency
"Simile: Willow and Gingko" by Eve Merriam., from *A Sky Full of Poems*. Copyright © 1964, 1970, 1973 by Eve Merriam; © renewed 1992 Eve Merriam. Reprinted by permission of Marian Reiner for the author. All rights reserved.

Lillian Morrison c/o Marian Reiner Literary Agency
"The Sidewalk Racer or On the Skateboard" by Lillian Morrison, from *The Sidewalk Racer and Other Poems of Sports and Motion* by Lillian Morrison. Copyright © 1968,1977 by Lillian Morrison. Reprinted by permission of Marian Reiner for the author.

National Geographic World
"Where Do Turkeys Go After Being Pardoned by the President?" by Bijal P. Trivedi from *nationalgeographic.com*. Copyright © 2004 National Geographic Society. From "Race to the End of the Earth" by William G. Scheller from *National Geographic World, Number 294, February 2000*. Copyright © 2000 by National Geographic Society. All rights reserved. Reprinted by permission.

New Directions Publishing Corporation
"Wind and Water and Stone" by Octavio Paz, Translated by Mark Strand, from *A Draft of Shadows*. Copyright © 1979 by The New Yorker Magazine, Inc. Reprinted by permission of New Directions Publishing Corp.

North Carolina Poetry Society
"North Carolina Poetry Society Student Poetry Contest" from *www.sleepycreek.net/poetry/submissionsstudent.htm*.

Pearson Education, Inc., publishing as Pearson Prentice Hall
"Poland: Tradition and Change" from *Prentice Hall World Explorer: Europe and Russia*. Copyright © 2003 by Pearson Education, Inc., publishing as Pearson Prentice Hall. Reprinted by permission.

PHOTO AND ART CREDITS